Images of Women

Corinne Miller

Lynda Nead

Griselda Pollock

Leeds City Art Galleries
1989

Bernard Atha

*Chairman of
Leisure Services
Committee*

**Christopher
Gilbert**

*Director of
Leeds City
Art Galleries*

In recent years Leeds City Art Galleries have organised a number of major exhibitions exploring popular themes in the visual arts, among them still-life and surrealism. This exhibition is devoted to a more emotive subject, the way artists have represented women, from Ancient Egypt to the present day.

For generations, images of women based on preconceptions by men, have lined the walls of our public art galleries. Their presence, meaning and implications for women today are rarely questioned. This exhibition focuses on four definitions of woman in relation to children, to men, to the home and to power, with an inaugural section considering the representation of woman as artist and muse. Arranged in small groups the works, drawn from wide geographical and historical contexts, invite comparison. Many share formal characteristics, some question conventional images and others challenge the supremacy of traditional fine art media – painting and sculpture – as an effective means of visual communication. The exhibition deliberately avoids a comprehensive or a chronological survey of this vast subject, but concentrates instead on the visual power of the works themselves in dialogue with the viewer.

Although the majority of these images were created by men, reflecting the usual balance of male and female artists found in public galleries, a significant number are by women. One of the most exciting aspects of contemporary art is the growing number of female artists tackling subjects which directly affect the lives of women, giving new meaning and validity to the representation of women in our visual culture.

Images of Women has been conceived and organised by Corinne Miller, Senior Assistant Keeper, Leeds City Art Galleries, and we are grateful for the inspiration she has brought to this task. Dr Terry Friedman has contributed to the entries on sculpture, while Judith Nesbitt has planned the supporting programme of activities and Nigel Walsh has assisted with publicity. We are greatly indebted to Dr Griselda Pollock, Senior Lecturer in the History of Art and Film, and Director of the Centre for Cultural Studies at Leeds University and Dr Lynda Nead, Lecturer in History of Art, Birkbeck College, University of London, for contributing the introductory essays.

The present exhibition would not have taken place without the sponsorship of Hammond Suddards, Solicitors, whose wonderfully generous support has made possible the lavish catalogue and the programme of special events. Art Galleries are having more than ever to depend on help from wellwishers and we welcome a chance to collaborate on this project with such an illustrious Yorkshire firm. We are delighted that their sponsorship has been recognised by an award under the Government's Business Sponsorship Incentive Scheme, which is administered by the Association for Business Sponsorship of the Arts.

Our thanks are also extended to the many lenders, whose names are recorded elsewhere in the catalogue, though a special debt is owed to Her Majesty The Queen for graciously lending the superb self portrait by Artemisia Gentileschi. The Museums and Galleries Commission once again has arranged for the exhibition to receive the all-important Government Indemnity; Heather Wilson and Stephanie Teychenne have been most patient and efficient in processing our application.

Vital help has been given by many institutions and individuals, in particular: Simone Alexander, Jane Baker, Dr Barley, Dr Bierbrier, Marcus Bishop, Sutapa Biswas, Anne Bukantas, Richard Calvocoressi, Jill Constantine, Brian Cook and his staff, Elizabeth Conran, John Coleman, Bryan Crossling, Mr I Donner (Director of *Double Two*), Stephen Dunn, Marlene Eleini (Marlene Eleini Gallery), Mr Fenwicke-Clennell, Dr Fowler and his staff, David Fraser, Ann Goodchild, Richard Green, Robert Hall, Lady Harrowby, Dr Hayes and his staff, Christine Hopper, Sarah Hyde, Jeremy Johnson, Sonia Lawson, Christopher Lloyd, Richard Lockett, Malcolm McLeod and his staff, Sandra Martin, Jonathan Mason, Mr K Matthews, Neil MacGregor and his staff, Helene Mitchell, Josie Montgomery, Dr Morton, Edward Morris, Michael Moody, James Neal, Keith Nicklin, Oliver Pickering, Alison Plumridge, Chris Pulleine, Sarah Riddick, Christopher Sheppard, Peyton Skipwith (The Fine Art Society), Margaret Stewart, Dr Stratford and his staff, Angela Weight, Louise West, the staff of the Women Artists Slide Library and Kai Kin Yung. Richard Easton, Jane Francis and Helen Preece deserve special thanks for their contributions to the exhibition as volunteer assistants.

Images of Women

HAMMOND SUDDARDS

SOLICITORS

D. Trevor Lewis
and
Alan Bottomley

Joint
Senior Partners

Since the nineteenth century many of our Art Galleries and Museums have benefited hugely from private benefactors. In these times when both national and municipal funding are scarce, our great institutions are increasingly looking for more support from commerce and industry. We are delighted to have the opportunity of responding to that need.

It therefore, gives Hammond Suddards the greatest pleasure in helping the Leeds City Art Gallery to mount this fine exhibition and produce this excellent catalogue.

We are sure that the exhibition will be enjoyed by everyone who visits it and congratulate the Director and his colleagues, who have worked so hard in its organisation.

Whose Images of Women?

Griselda Pollock

1. For a useful discussion of gender and difference see M. Barrett, 'On Difference', Feminist Review, no. 26 (1987).

We are all different. Each of us is unique. Yet we nonetheless share with other people certain characteristics or beliefs, and a sense of identity. Through these we fall into the larger groups which sociologists define in terms of class, religious and cultural background, sexual orientation, health, age and, of course, gender.[1] 'Vive la différance', say the French, celebrating the difference between the sexes as both fundamental and necessary. Men and women seem very different. But how, and why? Is it because we have different bodies, which vary in strength and appearance, and because of our roles in reproduction? Are these differences biological and therefore natural and unchanging? Some argue that they are not. Culture rather than nature dictates to each society and each epoch a particular and varied way of defining what is understood by a man and a woman. Sexual divisions are socially manufactured. Societies reorganise the materials of any basic anatomical distinction between the sexes to produce complicated and highly cultural patterns of behaviour, functions and definitions. They discipline male and female persons to conform to the socially produced norms of masculinity and femininity. Culture rewrites nature and thus what any society defines as a man or woman will change over history and it will vary from society to society. That every known human society has invested a lot of effort in ensuring the differences in social, economic and political as well as cultural and psychological terms, should not blind us to the basic fact that we are the product of social and not purely natural divisions. Gender identity will, therefore, also be affected by many other social factors and forms of social difference – age, race, class, sexuality, health, and so forth.

An important part of the way societies organise the difference of the sexes, what is known as sexual difference, works through images. We might understand images such as paintings or sculptures or photographs as mere reflections of the society which produces them. Thus, images are only seen to document how men and women are. But it is more often nowadays suggested that images are not mirrors in this passive way. Images actively create meanings for their viewers. In this sense looking at a picture is indeed like looking in a mirror, but what you are seeing is a created image which projects *at you* a way of understanding what and who you are. One of the primary functions of images or representations is precisely to create convincing and enticing versions of the socially defined identities through which we are invited to recognise ourselves.

Images are not only visual. Through art, films, television, magazines, advertising and the media, our whole culture is constantly creating identities and ideas about masculinity and femininity, about European, Asian, Afro-Carribean people, about working class and middle class people, about disability and sexuality which more often than not do not match our own idea of ourselves. Yet, they work upon our sense of identity, slowly imposing on us cultural, racial or sexual stereotypes or, sometimes, a more offensive racist or sexist definition. But it is also possible for artists to produce images which challenge received notions, expose the assumptions safely embedded in what we take to be normal and acceptable images of the people and the world.

Sutapa Biswas found herself working in an art school where she was the only Black student. Her teachers were all White and mostly men. Their references and knowledge referred only to European art and culture. *Housewives with Steak-Knives* [61] was one of a series of pictures she produced to challenge the Eurocentrism of her art education. The main figure is Kali, the Hindu goddess who is summoned to behead the devil. Evil is represented by the heads (Heath, Hitler, Trotsky) hung around her neck. In one hand she holds a sword, with another she makes the Indian sign of peace. Kali is an image of a woman composed of opposites which can be contained in her multi-dimensional persona. The heads are European, however, major political leaders who have been involved in Europe's imperialist exploitation of India which a renewed awareness of Indian culture can be mobilised to resist. In another hand, Kali holds a photocopy of a painting by a European woman painter of the seventeenth century, Artemisia Gentileschi, who painted several versions of the biblical subject of Judith and Holofernes. Judith was a Jewish heroine who was offered up to the enemy general Holofernes as a sexual hostage when her people were in dire straits during a siege. But, instead of becoming his victim, she and her maid cut off Holofernes's head and escaped, leaving the enemy in confusion and ensuring her people's liberation. Acts of political violence are not normally associated with women. Indeed, western culture typically defines women as passive – women and children to the boats first – while men take charge of politics, warfare and the law. Sutapa Biswas finds in Indian culture images of women as powerful and active; such images are not, however, recognised in western art history, from which the Gentileschi painting is taken. Judith and Holofernes was a very popular subject in the seventeenth century,

Fig 1
Peter Paul Rubens

Portrait of Susanna Fourment
c1622–25

*Oil on panel
National Gallery,
London*

2. *Burlington Magazine*, February 1962, p. 80.

but probably as a contemporary form of sex and violence movie. Gentileschi's paintings differed from many others made at the time by men because she used the subject not so much to titillate as to imagine women as brave and effective in so dangerous and political an action. Sutapa Biswas's picture puts India and Europe into confrontation, raising questions about politics, power and imperialism. She refuses either the stereotype of the meek Asian woman or the western stereotype of all women as passive and powerless. She uses mythologies from Indian culture to represent vividly a contemporary, historical dilemma which speaks to the experience of Black women in Britain, and speaks from that position to white women, challenging their limited and Eurocentric vision of what women are, can be, and can be imagined to be.

Thus, if we put the two terms, images and women, together, as this exhibition does, we are being invited to ask a lot of questions about what images of women are being presented to us across different epochs and cultures. We are being asked to do much more than look at pictures for their skill and aesthetic interest. Indeed, we are encouraged to *read* a range of images in many media. Reading is associated with writing, not with images. Yet, paintings and photographs and sculptures also tell stories and exhibitions can be read like a book. In an image a number of elements are put together to form a kind of sentence, or even in elaborate art works, a paragraph. A series of paragraphs, such as paintings hung together in an art gallery, begin to form a book which you read as you wander round. Taken together they convey a message. One of the major messages of most art galleries is that art is made by men. Until about the 1970s, very few art galleries exhibited any works by women artists. Indeed, so uncommon was it to even imagine that a woman was an artist, that the self portrait by the seventeenth century Italian painter, Artemisia Gentileschi [8] was not recognised as a self portrait. Instead the painting was thought to be an allegory of the muse or spirit of painting by an unknown artist. When in 1962, Michael Levy discovered the signature of Artemisia Gentileschi on the painting, and was forced to read it as a picture of a woman artist, painting about her commitment to the art of painting, he commented: 'perhaps the picture's real intention would have been earlier recognised had it been painted by a man.'[2] Contemporary artists who are women, like Rose Garrard, have drawn some inspiration from the tradition of Gentileschi and other women painters of the past in their current struggle to expose the negative assumptions about women in our culture today which continue to impede women's full and acknowledged participation in culture. Rose Garrard has reused Gentileschi's title for her multi-media work, *La Pittura: The Spirit of Painting* [12].

The misreading of Gentileschi's painting for two centuries indicates that women may experience problems with representing themselves as creative artists in cultures which generally define women as being merely procreative. This is not because they lack the necessary skills. Quite the opposite; Gentileschi's painting is a bold conception of an artist deeply involved in the process of painting. But the language of art with which all artists have to work is not their private, invented language, but one composed of social conventions and codes. The contradictions of this situation are apparent in the *Self*

Portrait by the French eighteenth century artist Elisabeth Vigée-Le Brun [4]. The historical moment in which she worked was critical for women. It was the period which culminated in the French Revolution and signalled the emergence of a new social and political system based on democracy and reason. The rallying cry was Liberty, Equality and Fraternity. For women the Revolution did not lead to greater freedom, but less. For the same social and political system that overturned the traditional power of feudal monarchy and demanded that people should only be governed by representatives they have elected, refused to allow women to participate in political life. Women were denied the right to vote and were driven out of their businesses and crafts so that they no longer had economic rights either. A new and very limited definition of women was invented. Women were to be exclusively domestic bodies, housewives and, above all, mothers. The division of the sexes which we today inherit, was formulated as a quite new idea in the late eighteenth century. Men were to be intellectual, political and active; women, emotional, domestic and passive. Vigée-Le Brun was an immensely successful painter working for the Queen and members of advanced and elevated Parisian society. Yet she presents herself as an artist in a way that completely contradicts the woman artist whom we know worked hard and regularly; and indeed, sat at her easel while in labour. Instead, we see a spectacle of femininity, a woman offering herself up to be looked at by the viewer, who can appraise her delicate features, charming and informal dress. She has made herself into an image synonymous with beauty. Yet, it is her exceptional skill as an artist, which has wrought the delicate features, the feathery frame of unpowdered hair, the silken gown and diaphanous shawl, and has taken on the impossibly difficult shadow first used by Rubens in a portrait of Susanna Fourment and rendered it as skilfully and convincingly (Fig 1). The painting is an ambitious, painterly challenge to one of the great Old Masters triumphantly carried off.

The first challenge which this exhibition poses is, therefore, to most people's sense that all artists are men. Many of the works exhibited are by women. But equally many works in this show are paintings by men. This allows us to ask the question if paintings by men and women are different. Can you tell which is which? Usually not by any stylistic criterion, or in relation to quality. But sometimes it does make a difference because men and women experience the world differently. One section of the exhibition brings together a series of images of motherhood. The *Maternity Group* from the Afo nation in Nigeria [13] dates from the nineteenth century. But it can be linked with a two thousand year old gnostic text used by Rose Garrard in her piece [12], for both offer us the idea of woman as Creator. The Afo sculpture celebrates the ancestral mother of the Afo people – an elevated and respectful sense of the founding Mother which Judaeo-Christian-Islamic cultures have displaced with a paternal creative function and Father, Masculine, God and Creator. Motherhood has, thus, been displaced – in Christianity the Virgin Mary has a place, but as the pure, chaste and passive vehicle of delivery of God's son. Yet, onto the features of the Virgin Mary how many artists have projected their fantasies and memories of their own dependence and forever denied passion for the woman who bears, nurtures and gives life and nourishment to every child. The image of the Mother as powerful and desired, as a source of anxiety and fear, as forbidden or lost, as overwhelming, haunts so many images of women – actually represented with children, or not, as in Dante Gabriel Rossetti's monumental but inspiring *Astarte Syriaca* [59]. The title refers to the ancient Assyrian and Semitic goddess Astarte, or Ishtar, a virgin mother goddess associated with the planet Venus, who was the life-giver and ruled without any male counterpart. In the section of *Post-Partum Document* [21] by the contemporary artist, Mary Kelly, the mother is not in the picture. The piece, composed of six sections, traces a history of the relationship between a woman becoming a mother and her child. By working at the level of the practical interactions of daily childcare (weaning, talking, teaching the child to write, answering its questions and taking the child to school) and the psychological level of fantasies, Mary Kelly examines the complicated process of psychological interaction and reciprocal socialisation for both woman as mother and child. This relationship is created in social rather than biological terms and, thus, she contradicts the dominant images of woman's 'natural' mothering. Instead, she invites us to recognise the desires and anxieties which women experience in this most powerful and misrepresented social relationship. In the form of a live performance, Bobby Baker [22] uses art to throw a different perspective on the experience of giving birth and living with a baby. In a humorous parody of American action painting in the style of Jackson Pollock, Baker uses bottles of Guinness, fish pies and lasagne to draw on a huge sheet while her running commentary

3. L. Tickner, *The Spectacle of Women: Imagery of the Suffrage Campaign 1907–1914* (London, 1987)

4. A. Davis, *Women, Race and Class* (London, 1982)

5. T. J. Clark, *The Painting of Modern Life: Paris in the Art of Manet and His Followers* (London, 1984) p.6.

recalls the bizarre and altogether less romantic aspects of childcare.

Bobby Baker and Mary Kelly bring out the fact of motherhood as work. Modern western societies hide this fact by the sexual division of labour in which women work at home without wages, keeping house and rearing children while being told that this is merely fulfilling their biological destiny. There is nothing natural about it; it is a historical and social convention. At several moments in the nineteenth and twentieth centuries it has been contested by women, such as during the suffrage campaigns and during wartime, when women's direct contribution to the war effort brought women not merely into the workforce (they were already there), but in greater numbers into

Fig 2

Dame Laura Knight

Ruby Loftus Screwing a Breech-ring

Oil on canvas Trustees of the Imperial War Museum, London

highly skilled and traditionally male-dominated areas. War artists such as Elsie Hewland [32] and Laura Knight were commissioned to paint women in aeroplane factories or engineering works. *Ruby Loftus Screwing a Breech-ring* (Fig 2) by Laura Knight represents a young woman of twenty successfully undertaking one of the most difficult and highly skilled engineering jobs in the factory, a job which she learnt to do in several months instead of the years male apprentices usually required. The complex machinery is painted with extreme care and attention to detail so that the precise nature of this task can be recognised. The main figure is treated as a portrait so that this is understood not to be any woman, a mere representative of the female working class. She is individualised and shows concentration on the job in hand. She is set in

the context of the factory where other women are also busy at their work.

The exhibition includes many idealistic visions of domesticity and women 'naturally' adorning the home; but such definitions of femininity were class-specific. Working class women were from the start of industrialisation one of the mainstays of the industrial workforce. They also formed the army of servants through whose low paid and long hours of labour the middle class home was kept bright and clean. Because of her servants the middle class lady could fulfil the ideal of femininity by being a lady of leisure in her home surrounded by children other women cleaned and fed. Working class women bore the burden of the labour in the factory and in other people's homes. But this was affected by the general middle class idea of what women were. So that despite working outside the home, working class women were also expected to labour within it—do the cleaning, cooking, mending and childrearing. While middle class women campaigned to have the vote, campaigns they could engage in because of their servants at home, Sylvia Pankhurst, daughter of the suffragette leader Emmeline Pankhurst, increasingly turned her attention to the situation of working women of East London. Trained as an artist, Sylvia Pankhurst complemented her political activities with producing suffrage propaganda. But she also painted, concentrating on images of women at work [28]. This in itself was a contribution to women's campaigning for political rights (lost since the revolutions which brought a male middle class to power). The suffrage women not only had to win a political argument in parliamentary politics, they also had to wage a campaign around images of women, convincing people that women who wanted to work and be politically active were not shrewish, hysterical and unfeminine, unwomanly women. They also had to show that the notion that women were safe and protected by male chivalry was not true, especially for working class women, who were exposed to both economic and sexual exploitation.[3] Nowhere was this truer than for Black women in Britain and in British colonies where enslavement and its legacy left such terrible scars. For the Black communities the mother, the family and the home came to have different connotations, for these were the spaces where some humanity could be protected and nourished against the inhuman exploitations inflicted by slavemasters and white society outside.[4]

It has been said that society is a 'battlefield of representations'.[5] Paintings, sculptures, photography, performance, video – all art forms participate in these contests for understanding the world, for promoting certain socially produced ideas and definitions, for examining and reworking our sense of who and what we are. This exhibition takes on this issue by posing some questions about images of women. Whose images are we offered? What notions of women, men, work, home, love, creativity and so forth do these images create? What are the effects of these different representations of femininity? How does the way in which an image is made, its materials, forms and skilful manufacture try to convince us to believe in the meanings it is constructing? What are the ways a new generation of artists who are women are intervening in this battlefield of representations of femininity, its social and psychological spaces, its pleasures and exploitations?

Bibliography

R. Parker and G. Pollock, *Old Mistresses: Women, Art & Ideology (London, 1981)*

R. Parker and G. Pollock, *Framing Feminism Art and the Women's Movement 1970–85 (London, 1987)*

R. Betterton, *Looking on Images of Femininity (London, 1987)*

Women, Representation and Power

Lynda Nead

The objects included in the exhibition *Images of Women* are drawn from an incredibly broad range of periods and cultures. An Egyptian bronze of *Isis and Horus*, a Renaissance *Madonna and Child*, a nineteenth-century Nigerian sculpture, and photo-textual work from Britain in the 1980s. In many ways the stimulation and pleasure of the exhibition lies in this diversity and in the juxtaposition of images which are not easily or usually seen within the same context. The categorisation of the history of art according to national schools, chronological periods and the *œuvres* of individual artists tends to rule out any thematic analysis or comparisons across cultures or conventional periods. In this exhibition, however, we are being invited to consider how women have been represented across a range of cultural forms and we can take this a step further and consider the effects and functions of these images within their given societies. Presented with such a diverse range of objects it would be foolish to try and assert any single cohering concern, any one preoccupation which binds all exhibits together; nevertheless, within the exhibition certain issues do take on a special significance. It is the way in which one such issue is reworked within different historical and cultural contexts which is the subject of this essay.

Fig 3

T. Jones Barker

Queen Victoria Presenting a Bible in the Audience Chamber at Windsor

c1861

*Oil on canvas
National Portrait
Gallery, London*

Although one section of the exhibition is specifically devoted to 'Woman and Power', this relationship of gender, representation and power is raised in one way or another by most of the exhibits. The question is, how do images construct or define both femininity and power; and what does it mean to talk of representing women and power?

It is important to begin by defining some terms, and what better place to start than with the concept of 'power'. Though we all know perfectly well what it is like to be without power, or what it is like to have power exercised over us, and also, to varying degrees, what it is like to have power, there is something residually difficult about defining power in itself. This is because power is always a potential, rather than a material possession. In French the word for power is 'pouvoir', which is also the infinitive 'to be able', and in both English and French, there is always this sense of the infinitive – in order to have meaning it must be completed with something else, being able... to do this or that particular thing. Power is always virtual, because it is never quite identical with an action or appearance. Power nearly always means the *capacity* to perform a certain action or actions in the future. And even when we talk about power *in* action (the power of a car, or a computer, or an athlete), there remains a tiny but crucial distinction between the action or performance that demonstrates or embodies power, and the power itself, which somehow lies before or behind its enactment.

Power, therefore, is never a state, but always a *potential*. It is like meaning in that it depends upon exchange and reception; the meaning of any utterance or text can never be said to be simply *in* that utterance or text, but must be activated in the contexts of reception and interpretation. This means that power, like meaning, is always produced out of social relationships. As the philosopher Hegel argued via his famous dialectic of the master/slave relationship: the master is always to some degree dependent upon the slave for his or her recognition of and assent to his or her power.

How does this help the question of the representation of power in visual images? For one thing, it may remind us that power is always more complex than simply a question of who has it as opposed to who does not – though of course it is always partly this sort of question – for power always works through networks of relationship. More importantly, it may suggest that the act of representation in itself sets up relationships of power. Images of women who seem to possess power, like Clytemnestra

1. Laura Mulvey, 'Visual Pleasure and Narrative Cinema', Screen, Autumn 1975, vol. 16, no. 3, pp. 6–18. For a development of this argument see Mulvey's later article, 'Duel in the Sun: Afterthoughts on Visual Pleasure and Narrative Cinema', Framework, nos. 15/16/17, 1981, pp. 12–15.

[60], Astarte [59], Kali [61], or Margaret Thatcher [54] in this exhibition, along with images of women who seem deprived of power, are never simply passive reflections of the ways things are. The image itself does not simply possess or lack power but establishes positions of power through the construction of a relationship between the image and its viewers.

The famous Armada portrait of Queen Elizabeth I [52] provides a useful example of this. At first sight, it seems an unambiguous icon of power, which simply asserts the glory and magnificence of England's Queen. But, as we know, there is also a special kind of uncertainty about

Fig 4

Sir Edwin Landseer

Queen Victoria and Prince Albert at Windsor with the Princess Royal

Oil on canvas Reproduced by gracious permission of Her Majesty The Queen

images of Elizabeth. As she grew older, she and her representatives grew more protective of her image, requiring painters to continue rendering her in her youthful beauty, while her costume and jewellery became more elaborate, as though to divert attention from what Francis Bacon called 'the decay of her personal attractions'. This is not precisely to say that Elizabeth was not as all-powerful as her portraits make her seem, but it is to suggest that the image of power is achieved in defiance of a particular insecurity, which comes partly from having to exercise power through an image. Elizabeth has to assume the role of custodian of her image, because of the fact that, as a woman, she is particularly liable to be identified with her image. Elizabeth knew as well as anyone about the power invested in the act of representation, and asserted her power through representation; but the very assertion of that power also bears witness to her dependence upon

being represented and viewed. In the Armada portrait, the very emphasis on the signs of power: the finery of her dress, the image of the defeat of the Armada behind her, the globe and diadem, all simultaneously assert the identity of Elizabeth with these symbols of power, and her distinction from them. The more the image says that she is both a woman and powerful, the more the excess of connotative material insists on the distinctness of the two terms: woman and power.

The image of Elizabeth focuses in a particularly intense way the uneven relationship of gender and representation. It is not that Elizabethan portraits of powerful men did not surround their sitters with the paraphernalia of power and riches, or that such men were not concerned to be shown as physically attractive; it is rather that this concern for the image is essential when it is of a woman, in a way it seems not to be for a man. This is because, in Western cultures for the last four hundred years, the very structure of looking has been asymmetrical. Of course, both men and women look at each other and are in their turn looked at by each other, but, as feminist theory has amply demonstrated, there is a clear tendency for the place of the spectator to be identified as male, and the place of the looked-at object to be identified as female. As Laura Mulvey has observed: 'In a world ordered by sexual imbalance, pleasure in looking is split between active/male and passive/female. The determining male gaze projects its fantasy onto the female figure which is styled accordingly.'[1] In the simplest cases, like some forms of pornographic image, this structure forces women into the condition of pure objects. In more complex images, but also in the more complex activity of looking at images of themselves and of other women, women may have the role of spectator, but in a narcissistic form, such that their gaze is directed on and scrutinises themselves.

Looking, under these conditions, enacts a drama of possession and control, in which women are not precisely powerless, but split between power and powerlessness, between active viewer and passive object. In the case of the image of Elizabeth, what we see is not precisely a woman *in* power, but rather a woman *and* power, a woman in a particularly highly-invested relationship to power. Elizabeth's frank and direct stare at the necessarily-unseen observer of the painting recoils upon itself, since it depends upon the necessary acknowledgement of her power by that observer. One might compare images of Queen Victoria, who seems at times consciously to have sought to be identified with the mythic figure of Elizabeth. Like Elizabeth, Victoria is presented in terms of national heroines, such as Britannia, particularly in the portraits of her as Empress of the British colonies (Fig 3). This act of identification is clearly an assertion of power, but is equally clearly an acknowledgement that power for her depends upon being identified with, or as an image. The difficulties attending this for Victoria are the more striking because of the popularity of images of her as a mother amid her family (Fig 4) as well as formal images of her as an Empress. To be split among alternative images and identities like this for a powerful woman is not to suggest versatility, but

Fig 5

Herbert James Draper

Ulysses and the Sirens

Oil on canvas Leeds City Art Galleries

vulnerability, and begins to undermine the claims to power that are being made in acts of representation

This is to suggest that in art of patriarchal societies the representation of absolute female power is always likely to be vitiated, or at least complicated, since there will always be, in varying degrees, a conflict between the assertion of power and the surrender of power in being looked at; to become an image of power, a woman has first of all, and dangerously, to become an image. The painting of *Clytemnestra* [60] by John Collier suggests this very clearly. Again, this seems at first sight to be an image of unambiguous power, the painting presenting us not with Clytemnestra as the wronged victim, whose husband has sacrificed their daughter Iphigenia, but the proud and unrepentant murderess. Clytemnestra stares unabashedly out at the viewer, with her chin tilted arrogantly backwards, and her right hand holding an axe not in the manner of a

timid novice, but like an executioner pausing for breath. But what is equally striking is how the painting circumscribes this affirmation of power. This is done principally by highlighting the ways in which the murderess is already an image. Clytemnestra's dress is carefully and artistically arranged, and her posture is that of a statue. More important is the curtain that she holds aside with her left hand, which along with the architectural details on the left suggest that she is an actress, who has either just made an entrance, or is about to leave the stage. To be sure, there is self-confidence in the way that the character holds the curtain aside and exposes herself to view, but, as the sign of the division between the real and the unreal, the curtain tells us that the woman is playing a part; that her claim to power involves a kind of artifice.

This relationship between power and imposture is particularly marked in images of sexually potent women. Dante Gabriel Rossetti's painting of *Astarte Syriaca* [59] shows the Syrian goddess of love staring commandingly out at the viewer, her two winged attendants clasping torches behind her. The parody of the *venus pudica* pose reverses the usual connotations of modesty, demureness, and exposure to the gaze, to suggest that the woman here takes control of her own image. The hands assert the lines of breasts and genitals and, in the form of the left hand and girdle, there is even the suggestion of a phallus – a visual threat which is given particularity by the fact that the followers of Astarte frequently castrated themselves. Like many other images of the *femme fatale*, Astarte's sexuality is self-sufficient, denying the pleasure of looking to the male viewer (and the female viewer installed partially in the place of the male viewer) and demanding, in the gestures that implicitly threaten violence alongside the languors of love.

But once again, there is an irony. For, like Elizabeth, Astarte depends upon being looked at for her potency to be acknowledged, and it is this very fact that compromises her power. For, of course, the *femme fatale* is no unambiguous icon of female control and self-sufficiency, but rather the result of a complex projection from male sexuality of figures of dread. Such figures simultaneously summon up dread and distance that dread in an ultimately masterable form. In this sense, Astarte is a split figure. The power concentrated in her unswerving gaze is a masculine power (Freud wrote of the close relationship between looking and sexual potency, and between blindness and castration), but her sexuality remains female. In upsetting the relationships between looking and being looked at, she also moves between gender-positions, in an unsettling play between activity and passivity. This is alluded to in the figures of her worshippers, who are of indeterminate gender, and in the overlapping images of the sun and moon that hover above her head. The sun and the moon are traditional images of male positivity and female subordination, and they embody a contrast between visual potency and receptivity which relates very closely to the structure of looking and being looked at; the sun as male, is traditionally considered to be the origin and giver of light (and in some Renaissance images, is also pictured as the eye of God), while the moon

2. *For a discussion of femme fatale images see Bram Dijkstra, Idols of Perversity: Fantasies of Feminine Evil in Fin-de-Siècle Culture (New York and Oxford, 1986).*

Fig 6

*Jo Spence
Jane Munro
Mary Ann Kennedy
Charlotte Pembrey*

Taking matters into our own hands
1981

*from Family, Fantasy, Photography
The artists*

shines only with reflected light from the sun. The sonnet which Rossetti wrote to accompany this image recalls these associations:

Mystery: lo! betwixt the Sun and Moon
Astarte of the Syrians: Venus Queen
Ere Aphrodite was. In silver sheen
Her twofold girdle clasps the infinite boon
Of bliss whereof the Heaven and Earth commune:
And from her neck's inclining flower-stem lean
Love-freighted lips and absolute eyes that wean
The pulse of hearts to the spheres dominant tune.

Torch-bearing, her sweet ministers compel
All thrones of light beyond the sky and sea
The witnesses of Beauty's face to be:
That face, of Love's all penetrative spell
Amulet, talisman, and oracle, –
Betwixt the Sun and Moon a mystery.

The sonnet stresses the power of sight, focussing on Astarte's 'absolute eyes that wean/The pulse of hearts to the spheres' dominant tune', and emphasising the way that her attendants 'compel/ All thrones of light' to be her 'witnesses'. The sonnet tells us that this goddess is primal, earlier even than the Greek goddess of love, Aphrodite, but also identifies her as symbolically subordinate to the allegorical parts she plays – she is Beauty, her face is the 'amulet, talisman, and oracle' of Love. It is for this reason that the poem is framed by these odd references to her mysterious inbetweenness of being 'Mystery: lo! betwixt the Sun and Moon... / ...Betwixt the Sun and Moon a mystery.' She is both origin and receptacle of light, both looker and spectacle.

Many other images of the *femme fatale* from the later half of the nineteenth century – Liliths, sirens, Judiths and vampires – also involve this projection of powerful or threatening women, usually by male artists, in order simultaneously to summon up and visually to control their power.[2] The viewer of Herbert Draper's *Ulysses and the Sirens* (Fig 5) is thus able to share vicariously Ulysses's experience of both 'succumbing' to the Sirens and listening to their song, whilst being bound to the mast and able to resist their destructive force. The power of these images cannot be said to lie simply in their subjects, but rather in the complex overlayerings of meaning and desire that run across them. A later and idiosyncratic version of this theme is Wyndham Lewis's *Praxitella* [57]. Here the emphasis is not so much on sight as on the idea of modelling and sculpture. The image concentrates its subject, Iris Barry, into a chunky collection of planes and facets, insisting on her body as a simplified mechanism. This is achieved principally by the visible transformation of 'female' physical curves into triangles, cylinders and polyhedrons, all of them emphasising the analytic activity of looking. The image derives its fearsome power from this transformation. It is as though to turn the flesh into mechanised geometry in this way is ironically to upset the conventional structure in which woman is viewed as passive object. Here, the objective body of the woman seems self-made, seems to defy the objectifying gaze. Wyndham Lewis's odd title for the painting, *Praxitella*, a feminised version of Praxiteles, the Greek sculptor, suggests this curious self-authorship. But once again, there is an overlaying of meanings, since this image of the self-sculpted woman is so conspicuously the product of an act of male looking and making.

This might be said to apply equally well to a more contemporary Iron Lady, Margaret Thatcher, whose images also inhabit a borderline between power and objectification [54]. The effect of Mrs Thatcher's carefully-tailored femininity, of voice, hairstyle and dress, is actually to suggest a certain kind of imposture, to suggest that she is merely playing the part of a woman. Paul Brason's image of Margaret Thatcher shows her as a kind of simplified diagram: although she is adorned by a rather extravagantly feminine bow, the real point of the image is made in the simple emphatic uprightness, which visually supports the slogan in no-nonsense sans-serif above her, '*The Resolute Approach*'. Margaret Thatcher meets the gaze of the viewer with frankness and resolution, while the other members of the Cabinet, most of them male, look around in a disorganised mess – and most remarkably, Denis Thatcher seems to be dazzled by the light into which his wife stares so unabashedly. This is certainly and emphatically an image of female power, but one needs to note the context of this image carefully. Once converted into an icon, by being painted, and displayed in the National Portrait Gallery, this image begins to be overlaid by the same or similar complexities in the positions of power as the images of Elizabeth and Victoria discussed above. She becomes a *projected* image of power, a kind of collective fantasy of femininity transgressing its own conditions; her power comes from all the ways in which she is not a 'normal' woman.

Recent feminist art has attempted to reclaim images of women and to present radical and progressive images of powerful women. There is the danger, however, that some of these images may perpetuate the problems already discussed, where power is seen as abnormal or transgressive and ultimately controllable through the conventional gendered structures of looking. Sutapa Biswas's *Housewives with Steak-Knives* [61] recalls and reworks mythical figures like the Hindu goddess Kali, who was created to destroy the forces of evil – defined here as racism and patriarchy.[3] But the irony of the image and its incongruously domestic title protect it from being reinstated as a fetishistic projection of the male fantasy-figure of feminine evil (the castrating female).

This disruption of codes and mode of irony is apparent also in the remarkable work of Jo Spence [36], an artist who uses photography to explore and resist the processes whereby women are constructed as images, and the relationships they have to those images.[4] Jo Spence's work

deliberately and often hilariously shows her simulating conventionally female images, sometimes drawn from the public world, but as often drawn from the private realm of family snapshots. The power of these images comes, not from the attempt of women to be identified with (and therefore *as*) images and objects which are endowed as symbols of power, but from the ironic *dis*identification of the artist and her fantasised image, the power of the implicit refusal of the status of image. Spence takes everyday, familiar images and makes them 'strange', exposing their conventional use and enabling new and radical meanings. In *Realization* [36] the pose of the woman with the bottle of washing-up liquid recalls the codes of TV advertising; but here the process of commodification is revealed rather than hidden. The background images and smiling mask, beads and wedding ring placed over the rubber glove point out the associations and dependencies of patriarchy, capitalism and colonialism. As the caption of one poster asks: 'Could you wish for anything more?' Spence's 'attack' on the potency of patriarchal images of women is accessible and motivating (Fig 6); who can deny the pleasure of 'opening fire' on those images from women's magazines?

The empowering force of images such as those by Spence and Biswas, along with much of the work now being produced by other feminist artists, lies in the knowing exploration of the complex conditions that relate women, power and representation. Rather than the simple identification of women with particular images that seem unambiguously to promise or embody power, this art engages with the power of representation itself. The work may involve a risk and the results may be provisional but this is surely the only progressive direction for 'images of women'.

3. For an interview with Sutapa Biswas see Hilary Robinson, ed., Visibly Female, Feminism and Art: An Anthology (London, 1987) pp. 37–42.

4. See Jo Spence, Putting Myself in the Picture: A Political, Personal and Photographic Autobiography (London, 1986).

Catalogue

The catalogue, like the exhibition, is divided into six sections. The inaugural section focuses on woman as both artist and the personification of artistic inspiration. It is interesting to note that the word for painting has taken a feminine form in language; for example, *la pittura* and *la peinture*, though traditionally practioners have been male. The sections which follow consider four of the most pervasive images of women, to which we may bring personal experience. In the second section, for example, whether as mother, offspring or as observer, we have our own ideas about motherhood. In section Three, women are associated with needle-skills, teacups – the provision and preparation of food being traditionally a female responsiblity – and the technology of the twentieth century, both inside the home and outside in paid employment. Sections Four and Five explore the depiction of relationships between Man and Woman in the Garden of Eden, and between men and women in societies ranging from Ancient Egypt to modern times. Finally, in an era when our first woman Prime Minister has consciously promoted herself as a powerful world leader, the exhibition presents various interpretations of woman as a wielder of power either through the authority of monarchy, wealth, violence or awesome sexuality, and sometimes, a combination of these characteristics.

*Numbers in square brackets [1–66] correspond to works in the exhibition. An asterisk * alongside the catalogue number denotes that the work is also illustrated in colour, between pages 50 and 67. Dimensions are given in centimetres, height before width.*

1

Thomas Hickey
1741–1824

An Indian Lady, perhaps Jemdanee

1787
Oil on canvas
102 × 127
The National Gallery of Ireland

This portrait raises questions which are fundamental to the exhibition: Images of Women: images of whom, by whom, for whom? It is the answers to these questions which determine our interpretation.

The subject is thought to be Jemdanee, the bibi of a Calcutta attorney and diarist, William Hickey, with whom she lived until her death, in child-birth. Bibis were common among the British community in India due to the disparity in numbers between European men and women. According to Captain Thomas Williamson, writing in 1810, such a woman 'under the protection of an European gentleman, is accounted not only among the natives, but even by his countrymen to be equally sacred, as though she were married to him; and the woman herself values her reputation.' Like the majority of Indian women living with Europeans, Jemdanee was a Muslim. Hickey wrote of her: 'Jemdanee lived with me, respected and admired by all my friends for her extraordinary sprightliness and good humour. Unlike the women in Asia she never secluded herself from the sight of strangers; on the contrary, she delighted in joining my male parties, cordially joining in the mirth which prevailed though never touching wine or spirits of any kind.' This entry, together with equally affectionate references in the letters of Hickey's friends, and the portrait itself, are all that we know about Jemdanee. However, they tell us more about the tastes and values of these privileged white men of the ruling class than the character of the sitter herself.

Thomas Hickey (no relation to the client) was born in Dublin but the lack of opportunity for artistic advancement in his native country forced him to emigrate. By the time he arrived in India, he was well versed in prevailing European tastes for portraiture, having worked at Bath and in Italy. This painting is executed with due regard to the accepted conventions of female portraiture. Jemdanee is dignified yet totally passive, resting against cushions on a colonnaded verandah (a popular feature of European homes in Calcutta), looking benignly out of the picture. She has become an object of exotic beauty.

Originally, this portrait was intended for a private domestic setting, probably William Hickey's own home. In 1787, the painter cannot have conceived that it would reach a far wider audience. Removed from its private context to a public art gallery, it now takes on new meanings as it is viewed by people from a variety of cultural, social and political backgrounds. Her haunting presence excites our curiosity; posing additional questions. What was it like to be an Indian woman living in a predominantly white European male society? What are the implications of being represented as beautiful and sexually desirable/available? What role have images such as this played in defining or constraining perceptions of Black women and perhaps most importantly, how does the context in which this painting is shown influence our interpretation of the image before us?

2

*Joseph (Giuseppe)
Ceracchi
1751–1801*

**Anne Seymour
Damer as
the Muse of
Sculpture**

*c1777
Marble
181 h
The Trustees of the
British Museum,
London*

Damer is portrayed in Antique dress, holding one of her own works, *Genius of the Thames*, while a mallet, chisels and punches – the sculptor's tools – lie at her feet. She was the only child of Field-Marshall Conway and his wife, Lady Caroline Campbell. In 1767 she married John Damer, heir to a great fortune, which he dissipated. Despite her social position and comfortable circumstances, Anne was determined to pursue the practice of sculpture seriously, which she did following the suicide of her husband. Her teacher was Joseph Ceracchi, a sculptor from Rome who came to England in 1773. Like many women artists of the time, Damer became the subject of rumour and innuendo; it was even suggested that much of her work was carried out by male professionals. That her practice as an artist was regarded as unnatural in a woman and more properly fitting to a man, particularly in the physically demanding area of sculpture, is illustrated in Farington's disparaging comments on her dress: 'a man's hat and shoes and a jacket like a man, thus she walks about the fields with a hocking stick.' After her death, a writer commented that it was remarkable that a woman of her beauty and position should 'distain the frivolity and frequently vicious pursuits by which females in the higher circles of society are unhappily absorbed and occupy herself with studies of an intellectual character' (J. Gould, *Sketches of Eminent Artists*, 1834).

3

*Mary Beale
1632/3 – 99*

Self Portrait

*1666
Oil on canvas
109.2 × 87.6
National Portrait
Gallery, London*

Mary Beale was one of the first professional women artists in Britain whose work has survived in any quantity. Her reputation rests almost exclusively as a portraitist but within the confines of this genre she was innovative. Little is known of her background. Her sitters were 'people of quality', her output prodigious and her mature career well documented in diaries kept by her husband, an artists' colourman and picture-dealer. Referring to her as 'Dearest Heart', Mary is shown as an experimental painter who used onion bags, sacks and even bed ticking for painting canvas. In this self portrait her hand rests on a canvas bearing portraits of her two sons, both of whom were to act as assistants in her later years, painting drapery. While the canvas and palette on the wall refer to Beale's profession, this is not evident in her dress. The swathes of rich silk whose lively decorative creasing enables a play of light to animate the picture surface, is typical of the period and recalls the manner of the fashionable portraitist, Sir Peter Lely, who had made portraits of members of the Beale family.

Elisabeth Louise Vigée was the daughter of a portrait painter whose premature death in 1767 left her without a teacher and she was, as a consequence, largely self-taught. Her husband, the critic and dealer, Jean Baptiste Pierre Le Brun, exerted a considerable influence over her early career, promoting her and providing access to a wide range of paintings from all over Europe. However, his extravagance and indiscretions eventually forced Vigée-Le Brun to leave him. Consciously modelling herself on the great Baroque beauty, Susanna Fourment, the subject of Rubens's painting *Le Châpeau de Paille*, Vigée-Le Brun displays the good looks which she used to advance her career. Her many self portraits (this painting was also the basis of an engraving) served to promote her image as both an elegant young society beauty and an artist even into old age. In her *Memoirs* she offers the following advice to artists about female sitters: 'You must flatter them, say they are beautiful that they have fresh complexions etc. This puts them in a good humour and they will hold their position more willingly. The reverse will result in a visible difference... Tell them not to bring their friends to the sitting, for they will all want to give advice.'

This seemingly innocuous painting provides a fascinating insight into nineteenth-century perceptions of the female artist, which to a great extent persist into our own day. Many male artists took on women as students, as the ability to draw and paint was regarded as a socially desirable feminine accomplishment. However, there is a lack of seriousness in this pupil's application to the task. She has dropped a tube of paint on the floor, reflecting a commonly held belief that women were temperamentally unsuited to the intellectual rigours of the professional artist. Women were denied access to life classes and, therefore, were unable to participate in history painting, which required the composing of numerous figures. Instead, they were relegated to less highly regarded subject matter like still-life (which this lady is, in fact, in the process of drawing). The title and symbolism of the picture suggest the paternalistic attitude of the painter towards his pupil, who looks to her master for guidance, like the classical nymph Clytie (represented in the marble bust on the table), transformed by Apollo into a sunflower and forever forced to turn her head towards the manly sun.

6

Françoise Sergy
born 1957

Around Woman

Performance by
the artist
3 – 4 November
1989

'AROUND WOMAN is a visual dance piece in honour of the common body. It integrates photography, dance, installation and music to explore the taboos and contradictions surrounding our attitude towards the physical self: hair, fat, shape, muscles versus the "perfect" woman's body.

Having worked as a performer with photographers for the past three years (Rosy Martin and Honey Salvadori) I was very keen to explore photography myself and devised a series of self portraits using slides projected onto my body, sometimes in motion, sometimes still. My main concern was to reappraise my own view of my body, to celebrate its own beauty, to work with it as a stepping stone towards accepting and cherishing an alternative role model.

Mainstream Western culture time and again defines the woman's body as small, thin, vulnerable and decorative, to the degree that only a few strictly coded shapes are seen as beautiful. They say only some people are *born* to dance, while most of us should be happy just watching. Why can't we be generous and accept more than one beauty and point of view (literally)? The issue of the woman's body has never been more political.

Throughout the performance I physically transform the space and the installation, as a symbolic gesture of control over my environment and over the complete visual process. I am an artist in direct, controlled communication with an audience. I am a woman in control of how I will appear to others. I have defined my own image. AROUND WOMAN is a celebration: touching, seeing, feeling, daring, flying... a common body which will never be the same: never again.'

Françoise Sergy, 1989

7

Val Robinson
born 1944

Self Portrait

1989
Oil on canvas
152.4 × 122
The artist

Val Robinson studied painting as a mature student at Sheffield Polytechnic. She takes as her subjects the domestic scenes which surround her as a mother of three children and as a painter. This self portrait is executed with her usual expressive layering and scraping-away of the paint. Devoid of all other accessories or the bric-à-brac of daily life, there is an emphatic, rather unnerving concentration on the canvas, the brush and the artist creating a sense of tragedy as the loneliness of the process of creation is laid bare. This is not an essay in image-making as revealed in the portraits of Vigée-Le Brun and Beale [3 and 4]; rather it is an honest portrayal of a practising female artist in middle age drawn from experience and delivered with an incisive wit.

Artemisia Gentileschi, one of the women artists to make a significant contribution to seventeenth-century painting, had an advantage over her male counterparts in that she could combine, in this one image, a self portrait and a well-recognised allegory of painting. She based the symbolism of the work, including the mask which hangs on a chain round her neck, on the description of Painting in the widely-read book *Iconologia* by Cesare Ripa. Like many successful women artists, Artemisia was fortunate in having an accomplished painter for a father. He could provide the training and the opportunities to establish a career which were generally denied to women. From her father, Orazio, Artemisia gained an understanding of the powerful and dramatic effects which could be achieved by contrasting areas of strong light and shadow, as practiced by the influential painter Caravaggio. Executed with a certain bravura, this painting represents a confident assertion of woman's abilities as an artist.

The personification of artistic inspiration as female has a continuous tradition which dates back to Antiquity. In the eighteenth century the influential painter and teacher, Sir Joshua Reynolds, wrote that 'we gravely talk of courting the muse in shady bowers', thus reflecting the commonly held view of the male artist in intimate creative union with his female muse. The decoration of this panel is typical of the sarcophagi produced in the eastern part of the Roman Empire at Docimeum, in modern day Turkey. The figures are set into niches which form an arcade along each side. It was common for individuals to associate themselves with cultural pursuits in their memorials. When this sarcophagus was transported to Rome, the roughly-hewn head of the man was finished to give a portrait of the deceased, who is shown here declaiming his work to the mask-holding muse of Comedy, Thalia. The Muses, always represented as young, beautiful women, were the nine sister goddesses, offspring of Zeus and Mnemosyne, who were responsible for keeping the Castalian Spring. This panel was purchased in 1776 by the avid and discerning collector, Charles Townley.

10

*Unknown
French painter
late 15th/
early 16th century*

**St Luke
Painting
the Blessed
Virgin Mary**

*Illuminated
manuscript
(Manuscript 8,
Folio 14v)
18.6 × 12.5
The Brotherton
Collection, Leeds
University Library*

According to legend, St Luke was a painter as well as a physician, and so he became the patron saint of artists. He is often portrayed sitting in his studio painting the Virgin Mary. The text on the opposite page is taken from his account of the Annunciation in the New Testament and, thus, the miniature explicitly suggests a direct communication of the miraculous event from the Blessed Virgin Mary which increases the authority vested in the Saint's account.

* 11

*Angelica
Kauffmann
1741–1807*

**The Artist
Hesitating
Between the
Arts of Music
and Painting**

*c1794
Oil on canvas
152.4 × 218.5
By kind permission
of Lord St Oswald
and The National
Trust*

The identification of artistic inspiration with the feminine, often in the guise of a classical Muse, accompanied the extensive use of the female figure to personify the art form itself. In this painting Angelica Kauffmann portrays herself grasping the hand of Music, from whom she reluctantly departs to follow the advice of Painting, who points to the rocky path leading to the heights of Mount Parnassus where Fame and Fortune await. This painting is essentially autobiographical, for Kauffmann, herself a gifted musician, had to make such a choice. The painter James Barry, wrote enthusiastically of this work in 1802: 'Some may say that this is great, since it was executed by a female; but I say, that whoever produced such a picture, in whatever country, it is great it is noble, it is sublime!' The composition clearly recalls the famous painting by Paolo de Mattei (now at Temple Newsam House) made into an engraving to illustrate Lord Shaftesbury's celebrated essay *Notion of the Historical Draught or Tablature of the Judgement of Hercules 1714*, in which the choice however, is between Virtue and Vice, both portrayed by women (illustrated alongside).

* 12

Rose Garrard
born 1946

La Pittura:
The Spirit
of Painting

1986
Resin, fibreglass and
mixed media, with
small TV monitor
and video tape
152.4 h
The artist

For I am the honoured one and the scorned one
I am the whore and the holy one
I am the wife and the virgin
I am the mother and the daughter
I am the utterance of my name

Adapted from an ancient gnostic text, *The Thunder Perfect Mind* (which is quite exceptional in Judaeo-Christian literature, as Hokmah – the wisdom of God speaks in female voice) this verse encapsulates some of the contradictory conventions which have shaped womens' lives and determined the way they have been represented in art. Spoken by Garrard and accompanying self portraits, which merge with those of notable and unrecognised women artists from history, the text becomes an embodiment of her struggle to reconcile these opposites through a study of women's role as subject and practitioner in history and her own experience; ideas represented by the double-sided mirror. The artist's dress bears prints of the virtuous ladies of Vermeer's paintings, while that of the model, who seizes her frame, thus taking some control of her own image, has prints of the more frivolous women of nineteenth-century painting.

13

Afo, Nigeria
19th century

Maternity
Group

Wood
70.5 h
The Horniman
Museum, London

This carving is thought to represent an ancestral mother, the Mother of the Afo people, and would have been owned by an individual village and kept in a shrine. Once a year such figures are taken out for the Aya ceremony, when the men make gifts of food and money to the ancestor and pray for increased fertility in their wives. The group, one of the finest examples of Afo sculpture, is unusual as it is not carved from a single piece of wood. The child on the mother's lap and the head of the child on her back are separate and fitted with wooden pegs. Moreover, there are two children instead of the usual one. The suckling girl child is actually a diminutive adult.

14

Egyptian
XXVI – XXX
Dynasties

Isis with Horus
the Child

664 – 343 BC
Bronze
22.9 h
The Trustees of the
British Museum,
London

The mother goddess has proved to be an immensely attractive deity for many great religious cults. Isis was venerated by the Egyptians as the mother of Horus, conceived after she had brought her husband, Osiris, back to life [45]. Religion in ancient Egypt embraced a vast number of gods and goddesses whose form changed from region to region and whose popularity rose and declined according to the beliefs of the current ruler. In this small votive offering, Isis has been assimilated with the more ancient goddess Hathor, often shown as a cow suckling a child, whose cow-horn headdress Isis wears. Both Isis and Horus have the emblem of a cobra-head, the uraeus, which indicates their royal lineage.

15

Pierre Bonnard
1867–1947

Grandmother
and Child

1894
Oil on wood
34.4 × 41.9
Leeds City
Art Galleries

Bonnard was an 'intimist', capturing the momentary gesture in everyday domestic scenes. Here he shows a grandmother, whose cropped silhouette, dominates the left of the picture. The peculiar angle from which this image is taken forces the viewer into an uneasy intimacy with the scene, focusing on the feeding of the grandchild and the relationship between grandparent and child. Bonnard used his relatives and friends as models and this painting may well show one of his sister's children while staying with their grandmother at Grand-Lemps in Dauphine, where the family spent their holidays.

16

Unknown French Painter mid 14th century

The Birth of the Blessed Virgin Mary

Illuminated manuscript (Manuscript 2, Folio 227v) 18.3 × 12.6 The Brotherton Collection, Leeds University Library

St Anne, confined to her bed and dressed in white, offers her tightly-swaddled daughter Mary to an attendant for bathing. This pristine image of motherhood set in a charming interior provides a curious contrast between the rigid formality of the Saint and her babe, and the intimate everyday scene of the preparation for the bath presided over by women. The text relates to psalms and responses to be used as part of the Office for the Feast of the Birth of the Virgin Mary.

* 17

Giovanni Bellini 1430/40 – 1516

Madonna and Child with Patron

Oil on panel 83.8 × 71.1 The Earl of Harewood

In fifteenth century Venice the Madonna and Child image was greatly revered and a specialised group of painters, known as the Madonnieri, grew up to meet the demand. This picture, however, is more sophisticated than their hack work. Bellini throughout a long working life exerted a powerful influence on the development of Venetian Renaissance painting, teaching artists such as Titian and Giorgione and introducing a greater feeling for volume and naturalism, in contrast to the decorative Gothic style practised by his father, Jacopo. Giovanni uses the architectural device of the parapet on which the Christ Child stands to delineate the space in front of the Madonna – which is also the space occupied by the spectator, while the brightly coloured landscape draws the eye into the picture. The patron, who probably commissioned the piece, fits uneasily into the composition, suggesting that part of this work may have been done in the Bellini family's flourishing studio. This is one of a group of paintings from the late 1480s and early 1490s where there is a distancing between mother and child; the child is displayed in a rather awkward pose instead of held closely to the Madonna. At some point in the 1480s Bellini married and his wife gave birth to a son but both had died by 1500.

* 18

*Joseph Wright
(of Derby)
1734–97*

**Sarah Carver
and Her
Daughter
Sarah**

*c1769–70
Oil on canvas
127 × 101.6
Derby Art Gallery*

In the eighteenth century new ideas of parental affection and responsibilities emerged. Writers argued that during a child's most formative years, parents should play an active role in the rearing of their children rather than leaving it to others. Sarah Carver and her daughter are portrayed with the greater realism and informality of the period. Dressed in fine attire and standing in a dramatically lit, stage-like setting, the mother is seen as fulfilling her natural role amid the abundant fertility of Nature. The bond between mother and child is strengthened by positioning their heads on the same level and by giving them a common focus: the exotic parrot, which the child feeds with cherries. This is an eminently feminine family group and only a modest reference is made to John Carver, Sarah's husband, in the miniature which she wears on her wrist. The powerful influence which the Madonna and Child image exerted over secular portraiture can be felt in this painting.

* 19

*Frederick,
Lord Leighton
1830–96*

**The Music
Lesson**

*c1877
Oil on canvas
92.8 × 95.3
Guildhall Art Gallery,
City of London*

This is one of a series of paintings inspired by Leighton's travels in the Middle East, where he acquired the silks and the musical instrument (a sas), as well as making the preliminary architectural studies for the background. Its exquisite beauty and sentiment has an underlying disquiet. The relationship between the nubile girl and the woman, whose girlish, seductively innocent looks are found in so many Victorian paintings, remains ambiguous. Is this a straightforward image of mother in her role as teacher, or of siblings? The exotic setting has uncomfortable overtones of the harem. We know only that the model for the girl was Connie Gilchrist, who had sat for Leighton since she was six years old. She went on to become a skipping-rope dancer at the Westminster Aquarium, where she was noticed by Whistler, who invited her to pose for *The Golden Girl*. As with so many of Leighton's images of women, there is an insidiously demeaning aspect in the superficiality of the music lesson, which seems to mirror the belief that the intellectual abilities of women were impaired by menstruation, as outlined in *Female Education from a Physiological Point of View*, 1884, by John Thorburn. In later years the artist was to help his sister in her petition against Women's Suffrage, and as President of the Royal Academy would not support complete membership rights for women.

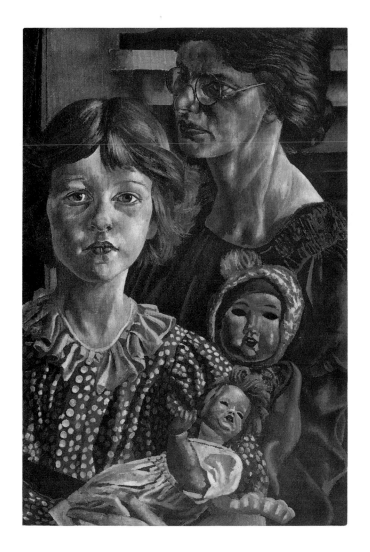

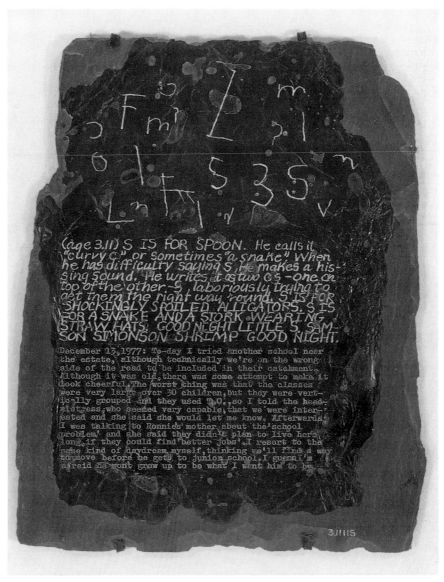

* 20

Sir Stanley Spencer 1891–1959

Hilda, Unity and Dolls

1937
Oil on canvas
76.2 × 50.8
Leeds City Art Galleries

Spencer's first wife, Hilda Carline and his daughter, Unity are the subjects of this portrait. It was painted at the home of Hilda's mother in August 1937, following Spencer's disastrous and fleeting marriage to Patricia Preece. Though divorcing Hilda, Spencer had hoped to maintain relationships with both women, pursuing the frustrated sexual desires he had for Patricia while enjoying those moments of 'special joy' in the domestic life he shared with Hilda. This arrangement proved unacceptable to both women. Nevertheless, for the rest of her life Hilda exerted a powerful influence on the artist, who visited her regularly and continually composed letters to her, even after her death. In this tense, claustrophobic portrayal of the family, Hilda's unfocused stare and Unity's engagement with the viewer rather than her mother, an estrangement intensified by the empty mesmeric stares of her dolls, creates a sense of confusion and deep psychological drama.

21

Mary Kelly born 1941

Post-Partum Document – Pre-writing Alphabet

Resin and slate 15 units, each 20.3 × 25.4 The Arts Council of Great Britain

Traditionally, images of motherhood have been determined by men and have stressed the natural procreative role of woman, or the paradoxical image of the Virgin-Mother, with its ideas of purity, youth and grace. Very few women artists of the past have attempted to present an alternative. Mary Kelly explores the emotional and practical side of motherhood. Drawing on her own experience, she creates records, which in turn become art works. The *Post-Partum Document*, of which only one section is shown here, charts her relationship with her son from babyhood through the early learning processes to his entering Infant School. In so doing, Kelly also examines how concepts of motherhood are defined through institutions, for example, the local health authority which designates 'the mother as guarantor of his well-being' in the yearly check-ups, and the use of the term Mrs by the education authority, to imply the child's legitimacy. The *Pre-writing Alphabet* takes the form of slates divided into three registers reminiscent of the Rosetta Stone, and contains the child's letter shapes, the commentary of the mother, and the Diary which records significant events.

22

Bobby Baker
born 1950

Drawing on a Mother's Experience

1988–89
Cold roast beef, skimmed milk, frozen fish pie, Guinness, Greek strained sheep's milk yoghurt, tinned blackcurrants, tomato chutney, sponge fingers, tea, black treacle, eggs, caster sugar, brandy and strong white flour on a white cotton double sheet
228.5 × 274.5
Performance by the artist (17–18 November 1989)

Bobby Baker trained as a painter but soon found it hard to express her ideas in paint alone and turned instead to sugar and cake as more expressive media. She found that the best way of presenting these edible works of art to the public was through performance. Among other things she danced with meringue ladies, recreated the history of modern painting in sugar, and made a life-size cake family in sugar-decorated prefab entitled *An Edible Family in a Mobile Home*. In the 1979 Hayward Annual she served the audience with a meticulously prepared *Packed Lunch*. In 1980 she had the first of her two children. In that year she took part in *About Time* at the Institute of Contemporary Art in London, but from then until 1988 she did no live performance work. *Drawing on a Mother's Experience* tells the story of those years and marks a 'come-back' to live art.

* 23

Unknown British painter
late 18th century

Man and Woman in an Interior

Oil on canvas
91.3 × 73.7
Leeds City Art Galleries

The neo-classical fireplace, griffin-shaped candlesticks and statuette of Flora on the mantle, testify that these are affluent people with fashionable and cultured tastes. The woman is shown following a domestic, suitably 'feminine' pursuit, tatting, while her husband is associated with the more intellectual pursuit of reading. The dog, a symbol of their fidelity, sits at the wife's feet. In *The Second Sex*, Simone de Beauvoir offers an interpretation of this type of image: 'man... will act as intermediary between his wife as an individuality and the universe, he will endue her inconsequential life of contingency with human worth... Queen in her hive, tranquilly at rest within her domain, but borne by man out into limitless space and time, wife, mother, mistress of the home, woman finds in marriage at once energy for living and meaning for her life'.

* 24

Frank Holl
1845–88

The Song of
the Shirt

c1874
Oil on canvas
48.3 × 66.2
Royal Albert
Memorial Museum,
Exeter

The skills which women used in the home were often those employed for financial gain elsewhere. The title of this painting is from a poem of the same name by Thomas Hood, which takes as its theme the plight of a needlewoman employed as a homeworker on pitiful wages:

> With fingers weary and worn,
> With eyelids heavy and red,
> A Woman sat, in unwomanly rags
> Plying her needle and thread –
> Stitch! Stitch! Stitch!
> In poverty, hunger and dirt
> And still with a voice of a dolorous pitch
> She sang the 'Song of the Shirt'.

Holl was one of a number of painters who concentrated on the hardships and misery of the poverty-stricken in late Victorian England. He sought 'to bring home to the hearts and minds of Mayfair the temptations to which the poor are ever subject'.

* 25

Stanhope Forbes
1857–1947

WRNS Ratings
Sail-Making

1919
Oil on canvas
106.7 × 137.2
The Trustees of the
Imperial War
Museum, London

The First World War opened up new opportunities of employment for women, as men left their jobs to fight at the Front. This painting, of WRNS Ratings sail-making on board HMS Essex at Devonport, shows women exercising traditionally feminine needle skills and working alongside men. As the necessity to control the use of images in the propaganda war declined, artists were increasingly employed simply to record various aspects of the conflict. Priscilla, Lady Norman was a tireless advocate for women's warwork on the committee responsible for overseeing the collections of the new Imperial War Museum. Originally she had concentrated on collecting documents and photographs, and it was not until 1919 that she turned her attention to paintings. Despite poor resources, she persuaded and cajoled artists to work for reduced fees and even to donate work. Forbes accepted £100 for this painting (a quarter of his normal fee).

26

Harold Gilman
1876–1919

Tea in the
Bedsitter

1916
Oil on canvas
70.5 × 90.8
Kirklees
Metropolitan
Council,
Huddersfield
Art Gallery

Gilman drew his subject matter from the life of the community around Camden Town in London, the theatres, bedsitters and people. The title of this painting is not original and imparts meanings and associations which the artist may not have intended; he preferred general titles, like *Interior*, to the specific. Though we know that the room depicted is his lodging at 47 Maple Street and that the young woman on the right is Sylvia Hardy, a painter who he was to marry in 1917, it is unlikely that this painting is supposed to be read literally. The all-pervasive bitter blue, insistent repetition of decorative detail, tilted perspective reinforcing the emptiness of the chairs and the lack of individualism in this barren room, combine to create an uncomfortable atmosphere. The small canvas on the wall stands-out in the centre but hangs in uneasy juxtaposition to the two women below. This painting is close in composition to the conversation pieces of the Eighteenth century (23), but in contrast to these images, where woman's role in the home is carefully defined and differentiated from that of man, the relationship of these women to their setting is unclear, and traditional definitions of the home are undermined.

27

James Neal
born 1918

Resting

c1940
Oil on canvas
60.9 × 80
Ferens Art Gallery,
Hull City Museums
and Art Galleries

Neal, who was born in London, has adopted Hull as his home town. He exhibited this painting in his diploma show at the Royal College of Art in 1940. It shows a clear debt to his teachers, Leon Underwood and Vivien Pitchforth, and has affinities with the heavy limbed solidity of the female figures of early modernism. In this candid slice of life Neal's mother is taking a break from the household chores and putting her feet up. The setting is the traditionally female domain of the kitchen, in her Islington home.

28

Sylvia Pankhurst
1882–1960

An Old-
fashioned
Pottery
Turning
Jasper Ware

Gouache on paper
45 × 33
Dr and Mrs Richard
Pankhurst

The Staffordshire Potteries were a traditional area of employment for women and many continued to work there after marriage (contrary to the norm in other industries). However, women never achieved the supervisory positions which were held by men and their wages were correspondingly lower. Christabel and Sylvia Pankhurst (the latter an artist who produced a series of paintings recording the lives of working women) were the daughters of Emmeline Pankhurst and together were founder-members of the Women's Social and Political Union in 1903, a more militant suffragist group than the National Union of Women's Suffrage Societies founded by Millicent Fawcett in 1897.

29

Graham Bell
1910–43

The Café

1937-38
Oil on canvas
121.9 × 91.7
Manchester City Art
Galleries

Women are traditionally associated with the preparation and serving of food in the home. These supposedly feminine skills made them natural employees in domestic service and catering. The female domestic servant or server to predominantly male customers has proved an attractive image for artists throughout history, as we know from the paintings of Chardin and Manet. What appears in this painting to be a simple rendering of an everyday scene is, in fact, a group portrait of members of the Euston Road School to which Bell belonged. The setting is the Café Conte in Goodge Street where members often met. Igor Anrep reads the newspaper and William Coldstream is closest to the viewer. In the background are Claude Rogers and Victor Pasmore.

30

Richard Hamilton
born 1922

Interior

1964–65
Screenprint
56 × 71
Whitworth
Art Gallery,
University of
Manchester

Hamilton wrote that his interiors: 'were attempts to explore how wild the perspective relationships could be, and yet be legible as a space... I discovered that there were practically no limits – that you could produce any number of wall-like faces in relationship to one another and it would somehow provide a... natural space, so long as there was some kind of furnishing in it, some kind of human being (to give) it scale... I will always have an opening into another space... I was trying always to establish the relationship of the external observer to the scene. If you provide something that's very close in a picture it somehow puts you, the observer, in the picture – you look over this thing into the scene.' The picture is built up with collaged images from magazines and brochures. The glamourous Sixties lady is removed from the modern world of a washing machine advertisement and placed in a more traditional setting (based on photographs of an Impressionist painter's home). Beside her, the painting on the easel has been replaced with the latest means of visual communication – the television. In this juxtaposition of old and new, of the handcrafted and the mass produced, the woman fulfils the conventional role of 'home maker'.

31

Arthur David
McCormick
1860–1943

Valve Testing

1919
Oil on canvas
76.5 × 102
The Trustees of the
Imperial War
Museum, London

McCormick was invited to record the highly skilled work of the WRNS in the Wireless Receiving and Valve Testing Room at Portsmouth. Commander J. F. Somerville (shown in this painting) wrote of this work in a letter (Imperial War Museum archive):

'The function of a wireless valve, which is somewhat similar in appearance to a small electric lamp, is to act as a delicate relay and detector and thus magnify to audible proportions the weak signals received by the aerial. The efficiency of the receiving apparatus depends to a very large extent on the reliability and sensitivity of the valves and each valve has to be carefully tested before issue. Valve testing was formerly carried out by skilled Naval wireless ratings, but as these men were urgently required at sea arrangements were made for them to be replaced by women testers of the WRNS [who] performed this difficult and technical work with such skill that failures in wireless communication, due to defective valves, were practically unknown.'

32

*Elsie Dalton
Hewland
born 1901*

**Assembling
a Hawker
Hurricane**

*1943
Oil on canvas
45.7 × 60.9
Manchester City
Art Galleries*

Priscilla, Lady Norman, who had proved herself to be a formidable advocate for the recording of women's work during the Great War, was made a Trustee of the Imperial War Museum. Her position and experience enabled her to exert considerable pressure on the War Artists Advisory Committee, formed in 1939 to organise a pictorial record of the Second World War, to cover the increasing participation of women. This painting was made at Hawker Aircraft Ltd in Slough.

33

*Dame Laura
Knight
1877–1970*

**Corporal
J.D.M. Pearson,
GC WAAF**

*1940
Oil on canvas
91.4 × 61
The Trustees of the
Imperial War
Museum, London*

Corporal Pearson was the first WAAF officer to receive an award: the George Cross, for her action when an aircraft crashed near the WAAF Quarters in Kent. The glamorous corporal sits before the idyllic landscape of the Malvern Hills, where Laura and her husband, Harold, were staying to avoid the bombing in London. The scene is dramatically lit in a manner more in keeping with Hollywood. The barbed wire and gas mask seem somewhat incongruous. As a student at Nottingham School of Art Laura Knight was unable to attend the life classes and found that segregation of the male and female students led to a greater concentration of teaching resources on the 'serious' students, who were all men. Laura Knight was only the second woman in the Twentieth century to be made an Associate of the Royal Academy (in 1927) and one of the first to be allowed to attend the Academy's dinners and banquets.

34

*Attributed to
Hendrick
Maartensz Sorgh
1611–70*

**Interior with
Woman
Washing Pots**

*Oil on panel
42 × 57
York City Art Gallery*

Great importance was attached to family life in seventeenth century Dutch society and this is reflected in the genre paintings of the period. The well ordered household was seen as a haven of rectitude and harmony, in contrast to the outside world where temptation lay in wait. As such it was the solid base upon which the newly independent country, a prosperous Protestant nation rid of its Spanish Catholic conquerors, based its economy and political power. It devolved to the virtuous wife to organise the household affairs and one of her primary tasks was cleaning. The obsession of this society with cleanliness went deeper than a love of housework; it was rooted in Calvinist philosophy. By moralising through easily accessible domestic images, Dutch artists could reach an audience with only rudimentary literacy. This painting was previously attributed to Quiryn Gerritz van Brekelenkam.

35

*Louise Jopling
1843–1933*

**Home Bright –
Hearts Light**

*1896
Oil on canvas
123.5 × 84
National Museums
and Galleries on
Merseyside (Lady
Lever Art Gallery)*

The vacuous subject matter of this painting belies the tragic circumstances and rigours of Jopling's own life. Following an acrimonious divorce, she was forced to maintain herself and her two children through picture sales. In 1874 she married the artist, Joseph Jopling, and set up a school for female art students, which she continued to run after her third marriage in 1887. The elegant, uncritical choice of subject matter and polished technical performance ensured popularity and a ready market for her work. This painting was exhibited under the title *Blue and White* at the Royal Academy in 1896. It was purchased by Lord Leverhulme as one of his 'soap pictures', with the intention of using it to advertise his famous products.

36

*Jo Spence
born 1934
and Terry Dennett
born 1936*

**Realization
from
Remodelling
Photo History**

*Photographs
50.8 × 76.2
(each of two)
The artists*

In these photographs, of a masked woman whose rubber gloves are like a second skin and naked breasts priced and served up as food on the kitchen counter, Spence examines the realities of food provision and its attendant household chores which are obscured in the advertising image of the glamorous, happy housewife. In collaboration with Terry Dennett, Spence questions the use of woman as 'food' for male photographers. So often, like the chicken which no longer bears any resemblance to a hen, the female model has no control over her own image. Through the self-analysis which informs her work Spence, who always uses herself as model, takes control and redefines the media image of woman. The collage of photographs and posters in the background represents some of the uses to which photography is put in our society, and illustrates some of the political and cultural determinates of life which are erased from the bland world of the advertisement.

37

Silvia Ziranek

**Anyone Can
Apron**

*Performance by
the artist
10–11 November
1989*

'I, ON THE FRINGES OF BEING A PERSON, HAVE BEEN ACCUSED OF COMPETENCE AS WELL AS GENDER. PLEASE! THE PROBLEM IS NOT ALWAYS SEXUAL, EXPENSIVE, OR INTELLECTUAL – JUST BECAUSE SOMETHING IS TRUE, I DO NOT HAVE TO BE UGLY AS WELL. BUT HOW BORING AND UGLY DOES ONE HAVE TO BE TO BE TAKEN SERIOUSLY? SOMETIMES IT IS JUST NOT CONVENIENT TO BE (MIS)TAKEN FOR A MAN... AND I AM NOT NECESSARILY PRONOUNCED MS. THIS IS THE GLORY OF THE STORY OF SUDS AND MY INNER BEING SAYS YES! I *AM* A TUPPERWARE PERSON. I SEE NO REASON TO PROTECT INTELLIGENCE FROM CLEANLINESS AND GLAMOUR. POST APRONISM?... CAN'T GET ENOUGH OF IT.
ON SPECIAL OCCASIONS, I APPEAR IN A STUNNING OUTFIT OF ALTERNATIVE BIODE–GRADABILITY AND FIERY (THOUGH CUDDLESOME) AWARENESS, READY FOR NON SEXIST, NON RACIST, NON NON NON (ACTIVITIES). I MYSELF ENJOY SMASHING UP THE WASHING UP TO THE SOUND OF THE LATEST HITS: PRACTICAL ATTITUDES, WITH A BOULEVARD TWIST. IF I CAN'T EAT FROM MY OWN FLOOR, FROM WHERE ELSE CAN I (EAT)?... WELCOME TO APRON ISLAND... AND IT LOOKS LIKE A LITTLE SPANNER SOUP FOR THE MEN, AND IF WE'RE REALLY LUCKY, US GURLS GET MASCARA PATE.
BUT WE CAN CONTINUE THE KRAFTSPIEL SPÄTER, LATER, WE'RE ALL *BUSY* PEOPLE; WHEN THE GOING GETS TOUGH, THE TOUGH DO NOT GO SHOPPING: CHACUN A SON IRONING BOARD. I JOLLY WELL SAY – OH YES, WE'RE ALL *PEOPLE* HERE AND FOR THIS I DO NOT REQUIRE THE MISOGENY OF THE MISANTHROPIC MEDUSAS OH EXCUSE *ME*. MAY *I* TRY ON *YOUR* EQUALITY? I INSULATE MY LOFT WITH OUTGROWN GOWNS AND MINI MIX 'N' MATCH MECHANICAL MANUALS.
I WISH TO REVIEW MY APRON STRINGS. I WISH TO WEAR MY BOLTCUTTERS TO THE BALL (TWELVE FOOT TWO IN HER PANTI-HOSED FEET)...'

Silvia Ziranek, 1989

* 38

Attributed to
Jan van Scorel
1495–1562

Adam and Eve in the Garden of Eden

Oil and tempera
on panel
58.5 × 45.1
Leeds City
Art Galleries

'Then the Lord God said, It is not good for the man to live alone; I will make a suitable companion to help him. So he took some soil from the ground and formed all the animals and all the birds... but not one of them was a suitable companion to help him' (Genesis 2: 18–19). The rest of the story about the creation of Woman from Man's rib is one of the most familiar in the Old Testament. In this painting we see Eve not only as companion to Adam in the Garden of Eden, but also, at the transitional moment between Paradise and the Fall, as temptress, provocatively entwined round the tree, her cascades of golden hair a symbol of sin. This painting is based on an engraving by Marcantonio Raimondi, which in turn reproduces the figure of Adam in a drawing by Raphael. However, there are several crucial differences. The print gives the drama a contemporary setting with a small village pictured in the distance. Van Scorel, on the other hand, adheres to the Biblical description of Eden and, more importantly, he excludes the serpent, leaving Eve solely responsible for Adam's transgressions. Having eaten the apple herself, she offers it to her mate. Luther wrote: 'God created Adam master and lord of the living creatures, but Eve spoilt all, when she persuaded him to set himself above God's will. 'Tis you women, with your tricks and artifices, that lead men into error' (*Table Talk*, 1569).

39

William Armfield
Hobday
1771–1831

Captain and Mrs Edmund Burnham Pateshall

1810
Oil on canvas
238 × 175
Scarborough
Art Gallery
(Scarborough
Borough Council)

The newly-married couple stroll along Lover's Walk in the garden of their home at Allensmore Court near Hereford. Like the Garden of Eden (which since the earliest depictions of Adam and Eve carried connotations as a place of joy and love), this English landscape is fertile and luscious. The branches of the trees are intertwined, reflecting the earthly union which has recently taken place. Mrs Pateshall brings estates with her on marriage which will increase the prestige and status of her husband. She is also expected to continue the line by bearing his children.

* 40

Arthur Hughes
1832–1915

**The Long
Engagement**

1859
Oil on canvas
107 × 53.3
Birmingham City
Museums and
Art Gallery

The shape of the canvas is like a narrow door opening on to a secret garden. In the microcosm of Pre-Raphaelite landscape beyond, a clergyman meets his innocent young love, their clasped hands symbolising the intended nuptials, while a faithful dog sits at their feet. Yet, all is not well. There is a pervading sense of melancholy. The burgeoning fertility of Nature stands in conflict with the chaste and unproductive union of the couple. The cleric, no longer in the prime of youth, has furtively stepped back into the shadows. The girl's name, Amy, cut into the tree trunk during the bloom of their relationship, is gradually being obscured by ivy (an emblem ordinarily associated with constancy). The landscape usually employed as an idyllic setting encompassing ideas of the joyous aspect of human love, is here turned into a claustrophobic environment which is consuming the couple.

* 41

Hugh G. Rivière
1869–1956

**The Garden
of Eden**

1900–01
Oil on canvas
123.2 × 94
Guildhall
Art Gallery,
City of London

Wrapped in their affection for one another, Rivière's couple seem oblivious to the world as they step out in a London park. The title invites comparison with the natural paradise of the Biblical Eden. But in this man-made respite from city life, there is rain not sunshine, and the leaves have fallen from the trees. The young lovers seem isolated not only from the busy world of cabs beyond the perimeter railings, but also from the natural world of trees and grass on the other side of the low boundary rail which dictates their way.

42

Arthur Eric Rowton Gill 1882–1940

The Adam and Eve Garden Roller

c1912 Portland stone and metal 76.2 h Private collection

Of those sculptors practising in Britain in this century, only Eric Gill and Jacob Epstein were bold enough to express in their work their obsession with physical union, a taboo subject in a society still hidebound by Victorian morality. Gill described Epstein as 'mad about sex', which manifested itself in explicit portrayals of pregnancy [56] and birth, while Gill himself dreamed of the very act of carnal love. In 1910 he had carved an exquisite stone relief (now lost) where naked lovers – the woman impaled on the strained arc of the man, her body crouched and coiled – reach ecstatic climax, which he irreverently inscribed with the title 'VOTES FOR WOMEN'. The composition reappeared a few years later, with the anonymous couple now transformed into Adam and Eve carved in low relief at each end of a stone garden roller, its cylindrical shape determining the figures' voluted forms. Gill imagined his own garden at Ditchling in Sussex as a centre of love-making and secularised the Biblical story: the roller was intended as a simple, everyday object (in which, literally, the First Man and Woman are having a roll in the Garden of Eden). Later, in *Art and Love*, published in 1927, he included an illustration of two figures coexisting as 'Adam and Eve in Heaven, or The Public House in Paradise'!

* 43

Henri Gaudier-Brzeska 1891–1915

Woman and Man (Odalisque)

1912 or 1913 Alabaster with traces of paint 20.5 h Leeds City Art Galleries

In his stone works Gaudier-Brzeska was forced, due to financial hardship, to use the off-cuts of his more successful colleagues, which he carved direct without the help of studio assistants; perhaps also his choice of a small, irregular block of alabaster for this particular work accounts for his decision to paint the surface red, yellow and brown. This must have given the relief a barbaric splendour when new, and enhanced the image of the vividly yellow, naked woman's primal power over man. The woman is awesome, stunning in her confrontational stare. The man, by contrast, is subservient: in profile, only partially revealed and positioned at a lower level, his eyes glued to the woman's breasts. The relief may be autobiographical. In Paris in 1910, Henri Gaudier had met a highly-strung Polish student, Sophie Brzeska, and in the following year they set up house in London as brother and sister, combining their names. From Sophie's published letters we know the relationship was a stormy one.

* 44

*Sir Lawrence
Alma-Tadema
1836–1912*

Pleading

*1876
Oil on canvas
laid on panel
22.5 × 35.5
Guildhall
Art Gallery,
City of London*

A Roman youth, in the role of supplicant, looks up to the woman, on whose lap lies a bunch of roses, one of the attributes of Venus, goddess of love. The poisonous oleander which towers over the parapet strikes an ominous chord. The woman, whose Victorian features are somewhat at odds with the classical setting, seems self-absorbed and lacks any forceful personality. Her apparent torpor and anti-intellectualism were typical character traits applied to the 'fair sex' in the nineteenth century. The story which lies behind this work, as so often in Alma-Tadema's art, is obscure. Indeed, some scholars have argued that his attention to detail detracts from the central issue of his paintings, and suggest that he found it difficult, if not impossible, to confront human psychology. The mental breakdown suffered by his wife, and his daughter's periods of mental illness may not be insignificant.

45

*Egyptian
XXVI Dynasty*

Isis and Osiris

*c530 BC
Schist
81.3 h
The Trustees of the
British Museum,
London*

Osiris was a beneficent ruler of Egypt whose reign came to an end when his jealous brother, Seth, attempted to drown him in a golden coffin. Osiris's sister and wife, Isis, recovered the body but Seth seized it and cut it up into fourteen pieces, which he threw into the Nile. Isis sought out each piece and reconstituted the figure. By transforming herself into a kite and flapping her wings, she created a breeze to breathe new life into the dead body. From her resurrected husband she conceived a son, Horus (14), who was to avenge his father's death. In this statue, the mummiform figure of Osiris, as God of the Dead, is dwarfed by Isis, who enshields him, a powerful protectress as well as the giver of new life. The inscription testifies that this statue was dedicated by Sheshonq, Steward to Ankhnesheferibre, a celibate priestess who ruled Southern Egypt, though in practice power was exercised by the Steward himself. One wonders if the fact that Sheshonq was in the service of a woman influenced him in his choice of Isis for his votive statue.

46

Adriaen van Utrecht 1599–1652

Still Life with Two Lovers

1631
Oil on canvas
132.2 × 185.4
The Bowes Museum, Barnard Castle, County Durham

The ambiguity of the relationship between man and woman, suggested in the paintings of Tissot and Lichtenstein [50 and 49], is here made explicit. In this lascivious scene the lovers stand before a table laden with a cornucopian still-life of fruit, vegetables and game. The availability of such exotic food-stuffs in Antwerp attracted artists like Van Utrecht to the city, where he became one of the leading still-life painters. While the allegorical significance of each item in this painting cannot be identified, their excessive abundance suggests a sense of overwhelming, even overripe fertility. The inclusion of a monkey, perceived as a baser form of human, is a symbol of vice or lust.

47

Elaine Kowalsky born 1946

Yakity Yak (Love Talk)

1986
Oil on paper
122 × 162.6
The artist

'I love your lips.
Your feet are like ice.
Scratch my back?
You got great hips.
Who fed the cat?
How can you say that?
I like your toes.
You forgot to clean the bath.
I don't like your family.
Want a cup of tea?
What about me?
Can you iron my shirt?
I just emptied the cat dirt!
Give me a hug.

Love Talk
Yakity yak, love talk the on going dialogue that goes on and on from the first mutterings of courtship to the emergence of a relationship out of the cocoon of an affair. The talking, arguing and daily nattering goes on and on. The two cartoon figures in the painting are anybody woman and anybody man from the latter half of the twentieth century. Yakity yak Love Talk.'

Elaine Kowalsky, 1989

* 48

*Andrea Fisher
born 1955*

In Silence II

*1989
Cibachrome and
sculptural object
122 × 274 × 61
By courtesy of the
Marlene Eleini
Gallery, London*

'Through the juxtaposition of a cinematic image and a Minimalist object, *In Silence II* explores an aesthetisisation of violence which extends from the media into fine art practise.

In the image, a hand intrudes into the interior of a car; through the rear window a woman is glimpsed as she falls. Yet it remains unclear whether she has surrendered in ecstasy, or to a violation. In her image, violence and eroticism coalesce. And perhaps it is precisely the intimation of violence which redoubles our fascination with her fall; for current notions of femininity create a frisson around a woman's languor, passivity, surrender to force and even death.

The sculptural object parallels the image through the play of force at the heart of its aesthetic. Minimalism presented itself as a final distillation of pure form, without reference to its social context. But it was an art of sleek corporate form, produced by industrial processes. As such, it was embedded in a culture celebrating its industrial achievements.

The pleasure of the Minimalist object lies, at least in part, in the immutable power of its machine made presence. The demand that great art should 'overpower' us seems now so entrenched that power can become indistinguishable from beauty (and our seduction by power in art may spill over into our relations with power elsewhere). Both the image and the sculptural object explore aesthetic codes in which visual pleasure surrounds the presence of force. Yet the piece does not obstruct such pleasures. By creating a place for them, it creates a place for us to contemplate our ambivalent involvement with them.'

Andrea Fisher, 1989

* 49

*Roy Lichtenstein
born 1923*

In the Car

*1963
Magna on canvas
172 × 203.5
Scottish National
Gallery of Modern
Art, Edinburgh*

Lichtenstein once described his subject as 'The most brazen characteristics of our culture, things we hate, but which are also powerful in their improvement on us'. *In the Car* is based on the comic strip cartoon. The paint surface is given a slick, almost perfect finish which removes all evidence of the artist's part in its creation, allying it to the images of mass-produced urban culture which proved so attractive to American Pop artists. The huge magnification and lurid primary colours intensify the latent violence of the subject. In contrast to the equitable positions of the man and woman in Kowalsky's painting [47], who seem destined eternally to confront each other but never to touch, Lichtenstein's figures are packed tightly together. The handsome young man clothed in the formal collar and tie of civilisation grips the wheel of his car as he steals a look at the cool, self-assured blonde beside him, her leopard-skin coat not only a symbol of wealth but of the primal animal nature of her sexuality.

50

James Jacques Tissot 1836–1902

The Bridesmaid

c1883–85 Oil on canvas 147.3 × 101.6 Leeds City Art Galleries

The series of fifteen paintings entitled *La Femme à Paris* which Tissot first exhibited in 1885 included a fashionable lady, a provincial lady, a political woman, a shop assistant, a gossip and a bridesmaid. Minutely observed and meticulously painted these images of middle class women found a ready market. Nevertheless, the series also allowed him to explore the social context of women. What at first sight may appear a rather superficial moment in the lives of the subjects is filled with details which pose questions about prevailing Victorian attitudes to marriage. The bridesmaid stands alone in her vivid blue dress on an otherwise empty patch of pavement, set off against the dark colours of the coach, the groom, the camera boy, the on-looking crowd and the bustle of the street. She is unsteady as she leans forward to wave goodbye. The groom, whose face is so intimately associated with hers, eyes her rakishly while tucking his bride into the coach, where she is already hidden from both the spectator and the world. In the background two shop girls sigh with longing. Tissot must himself have given much thought to the position of women with regard to marriage during his liaison with Irish divorcee, Kathleen Newton, with whom he lived from 1876 to 1882, making her the subject of many of his paintings, even after her slow-lingering death from consumption.

51

Rachael Field born 1965

Heroes

1988 Oil on canvas 91.5 × 61 The artist

'Subverting the general ideal of what women should look like and how we should behave is a constant theme of my art. In my paintings and drawings I also deal with an issue that daily affects my life, that is the fear and therefore hatred of lesbians.

I live and work with my partner Nenagh but although our relationship is long term, it is often unacknowledged in an environment of presumed heterosexuality. To be honest about our lesbianism we have to make the decision to take risks. Physical closeness in public of heterosexual couples can be taken for granted but we face censure, abuse and incredulity.

Feeling no desire to attract the opposite sex, Nenagh and I do not conform to prescribed femininity. Thus without the trappings that construct how women are perceived, we are wrongly accused of wanting to be like men. 'What are they?', is a comment often made about us and the women in my paintings; reflecting the anger caused by not comprehending the rejection of the conventional female stereotype.

HEROES depicts a typical incident of verbal abuse but in painting it I have reclaimed control. Documenting our lesbian experience counteracts the images of women that are imposed to restrict our lives.'

Rachael Field, 1989

* 52

Unknown British painter

Armada Portrait of Queen Elizabeth I

*c1588–89
Oil on panel
113 × 128
W. Tyrwhitt-Drake, Esq.*

In the course of her long reign, Elizabeth became a cult figure portrayed in two roles, defined by Edmund Spenser as 'a most royall Queene or Empresse' and 'a most vertuous and beautiful Lady'. Demand for her likeness was so great that in order to control her image, and promote herself as a powerful leader into old age, portraits were all derived from a few officially approved samples. Thus, more than one version of this painting exists. (This one is thought to have been commissioned by Sir Francis Drake.) Completed after the defeat of the Armada in 1588, the portrait takes its name from the two vignettes, which show the Spanish fleet sailing towards England and, on the right, being wrecked off the coast of Scotland. The icon-like ruler is surrounded by the attributes of power: the terrestrial globe, costly jewels and fabrics, and the Imperial crown. Tudor monarchs attached tremendous importance to their closed crown, reflecting equality of status with the Holy Roman Emperor.

53

*William Ernest Reynolds-Stephens
1862–1943*

A Royal Game

*1906–11
Various metals
and inlays
241.3 h
The Trustees of the
Tate Gallery, London*

Reynolds-Stephens reinterprets the Armada story in the form of a fictitious game of chess between Elizabeth I and a genuflecting Philip II of Spain. In this intensely chauvenistic sculpture, the artist uses the great Tudor monarch as an allegory for the 'glories' of Edwardian Imperialism. In his article *A British Fine Art Ministry*, published in 1911, he called for a Ministry to regulate and promote the arts in 'the period of our greatness' and to give recognition 'to the importance of their place in the national life and their power indelibly to record our history and times', for he asserted, 'The great mass of the finest art has been national – the outcome of the thought of the time and peoples for which it was produced'.

Margaret Thatcher, the first woman to become Prime Minister, has assumed a carefully constructed image combining the soft silky bows of femininity with the authority vested in the tailored city suit. Mr Stanton D. Loring, an American admirer, commissioned this portrait of the PM addressing the Conservative Party Conference held at Brighton in 1982, shortly after the Falklands War. From left to right, the sitters are Sir Geoffrey Howe, Cecil Parkinson, Ann Parkinson, Mr and Mrs Denis Thatcher and Francis Pym. Mr Loring writes: 'In commissioning Mr Brason, I requested a portrait of Mrs Thatcher that would evoke in the viewer a sense that here indeed was a gallant leader who characterized all the traditional strength of the British spirit. In my view Mrs Thatcher personified these qualities, particularly in the quiet dynamics she displays when talking before groups of people'. This image of the 'gallant leader' is in striking contrast to the soft-focus, feminine, official portrait commissioned by the National Portrait Gallery from Rodrigo Moynihan, to which Mrs Thatcher put forward a number of criticisms.

The goddess is amongst the most potent symbols of female power. This Egyptian example is one of about six hundred statues of Sekhmet originally set up in the mortuary temple of Amenophis III at Thebes, where offerings were made for the well-being of the late king in his after-life. Sekhmet was fiercely protective of the sun god Ra, and was the object of special veneration by Amenophis. In her hand is the ankh sign, the symbol of life, while on her head she wears a solar disc. The identification of the gods with animals, birds and reptiles goes back to a time when each locality worshipped an animal or an inanimate object. Gradually anthropomorphism took over so that gods like Sekhmet have a human body with a beast's head.

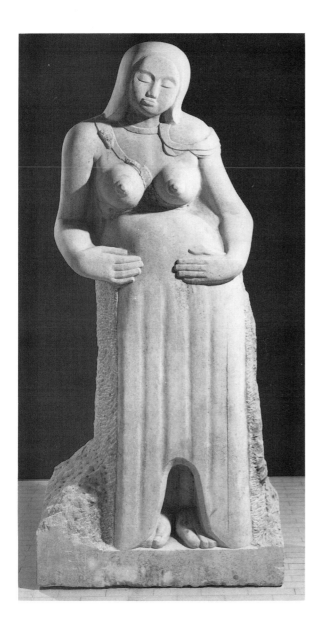

56

Sir Jacob Epstein
1880–1959

Maternity

c1910–12
Hoptonwood stone
206 h
Leeds City
Art Galleries

This is one of a group of stone carvings concerned with ideas of sexual desire, fecundity and birth which preoccupied the young Epstein. This particular work was probably intended as part of a 'great scheme for doing some colossal figures together (as a contribution to the world), a sort of twentieth-century Stonehenge', which Epstein and Gill intended to construct around 1910. The other sculptures may have included the *Sun God* relief, a projected columnar group of an embracing couple and a totem depicting copulation and birth – expressive of Epstein's vision of a shrine 'apotheosising Man and Woman' – together with Gill's relief of *Ecstasy*. At this time both sculptors sought inspiration in non-Western cultures to whom issues of fertility, both in their women and their crops, were of central importance to the survival of their society. The sitter for *Maternity* was an Irish girl named Marie Rankin, who, through the influence of Hindu erotic sculpture, is transformed into a young contemplative woman in control of her destiny and that of her unborn child, this most poignant aspect lovingly conveyed by the arms and hands cradling the pregnant womb. Though the 'Stonehenge' project failed due to lack of funds, the process of birth endures as a powerful image in *Maternity* through the unfinished state of the carving, which exposes the lower limbs eternally struggling to emerge from the block of raw stone.

57

Percy Wyndham
Lewis
1882–1957

Praxitella

1921
Oil on canvas
142.2 × 101.6
Leeds City
Art Galleries

Iris Barry, the painter's mistress and the Praxitella of this portrait, has been transformed into a formidable robotic female whose eyelids are like sheets of metal restraining fearsome fiery eyes, reminiscent of the shiny metal surfaces and awesome power of the guns which so impressed Lewis during active service in the First World War. He pronounced himself 'a fanatic for the externality of things' and adopted a 'fleshed-out' version of the Cubist idiom to portray the character of his sitters through their exterior form. Iris was part of the London literary circle which included Ezra Pound and the artist himself. She was a founder-member of the London Film Society and went on to become the first curator of the film library at the Museum of Modern Art in New York.

* 58

Jonathan Richardson 1665–1745

Lady Mary Wortley Montagu in Turkish Dress

c1720–25
Oil on canvas
238.8 × 144.8
The Earl of Harrowby

In 1712 Mary Pierrepont (1689–1762) married Edward Wortley Montagu against her father's wishes and accompanied him to Constantinople on his appointment as ambassador. In this portrait she has adapted her western dress to give it a vaguely Turkish 'air'. The marriage was unhappy and in 1739 she left England in pursuit of a young Italian writer, Count Francesco Algarotti, for whom she had conceived a passion, and did not return until the year of her death from breast cancer in 1762. A prolific letter writer, and widely admired in her own time as a traveller and wit, Mary has left a vivid insight into issues relating to women in the eighteenth century. In a letter to her husband in 1714 she observed: '... tis a sort of duty to be rich, that it may be in one's power to do good, riches being another word for power'.

* 59

Dante Gabriel Rossetti 1828–82

Astarte Syriaca

1877
Oil on canvas
182.9 × 106.7
Manchester City Art Galleries

Rossetti was a gifted poet and painter and a founder member of the secret society of painters known as the Pre-Raphaelite Brotherhood. In later years he began to explore the theme of the *femme fatale* (through legendary figures like Astarte), a woman whose terrifying sexual power over man could prove fatal. His model for these paintings was Jane Morris, wife of William Morris, with whom he fell passionately in love. Described by Henry James as the 'dark, silent, medieval woman', her exceptional looks made her a legend in her own life time, but fame brought its own problems, as Graham Robertson wrote: 'Mrs Morris required to be seen to be believed, and even then she was dreamlike... I fancy that her mystic beauty must sometimes have weighed rather heavily upon her'. The immense popularity of the *femme fatale* in literature and art came at a time of great advances in the rights of women with the Matrimonial Causes Act of 1857, the first Parliamentary debate on Women's Suffrage in 1867 and the Married Woman's Property Act of 1870.

* 60

*The Hon
John Collier
1850–1934*

Clytemnestra

*1882
Oil on canvas
238.8 × 147.3
Guildhall
Art Gallery
City of London*

Clytemnestra is shown holding the bloody axe which she used to kill her husband, Agamemnon. She was driven to seek revenge for the sacrifice of their daughter, Iphigenia, to appease the goddess Diana (thus ensuring favourable winds for the Greek fleet) and the seizing and raping of Cassandra, daughter of King Priam of Troy. John Collier chose to depict not the pathos of the wronged woman, but the more dramatic theme of woman driven by a passion tantamount to madness, to commit a violent act out of keeping with concepts of feminine behaviour. Like his contemporary, Alma-Tadema, Collier strove to achieve archaeological accuracy. He took great care rendering the architectural paraphernalia, which includes a column from the Treasury of Atreus at Mycenae (sometimes referred to as the Tomb of Agamemnon). Victorian reconstructions of the entrance to this ancient building incorrectly placed the richly moulded capital of the column at its base, and the error is repeated in this painting. Two years before, in 1880, Oxford undergraduates gave the first performance in the original Greek of Aeschylus's tragedy *Agamemnon* at Balliol College, and a subsequent performance in London at St George's Hall. The part of Clytemnestra, in accordance with the conventions of Greek tragedy, was played by a man, Frank Benson. If Collier was basing this study on his knowledge of the theatre, it would account for the masculinity of the female figure.

* 61

*Sutapa Biswas
born 1962*

**Housewives
with Steak-
Knives**

*1985
Oil, acrylic and
pastel on paper
and canvas
274 × 244
The artist*

In re-working the goddess image, women artists have sought to construct new representations of female power. Biswas portrays herself as the ferocious many-armed Kali, a Hindu goddess who is both protectress and destroyer of evil (the choice has great personal significance as the artist's grandmother was a devotee of Kali). Around her neck is the traditional garland of mens' heads. Although none of these gruesome accoutrements is a true likeness, the unmistakable features of Trotsky and Hitler can be discerned. The calm side of Kali's personality is represented by the rose, a symbol of peace. In the same hand she holds two collaged reproductions of famous works by women artists from the past: *Judith and Holofernes* by Artemisia Gentileschi (discussed in Griselda Pollock's essay in this catalogue) and another picture of the same subject by Elisabetta Sirani. The inclusion of a work by Gentileschi, whose rape by one of her father's friends, the painter Agostino Tassi, and the well-documented traumas of her torture by the court to force a retraction of her allegations (which she refused to do), and her assailant's subsequent trial, is particularly appropriate in this context. Dressed in the colours of anarchy, red and black, this heroic goddess battles with the evils of capitalism, racism and patriachy.

62

Henry Moore
1898–1986

**Mother
and Child**

1936
Green Hornton
stone
114.2 h
Leeds City
Art Galleries

In the 1930s Moore reduced the formal elements of primitive art which had fascinated him during the previous decade (65) to their essentials, in order to generate an all-embracing sense of primal power, neither Western nor Christian in concept, in his mother and child groups. In this sculpture a single cylindrical solid is enwrapped by a few, rudimentary yet universal signs for the human body: a pair of eyes, a hair-bun, a solitary arm cradling the softer shape of the infant. However, such simplification does not obscure the message of this strange, heroic carving. One day in 1937, Roland Penrose, the doyen of British Surrealism, took the painter Max Ernst on a visit to Moore's studio in Hampstead, where they were shown various sculptures 'draped mysteriously in white sheets'. One of these, uncovered, revealed a 'bird-like' figure 'both male and female in implication', that is, phallic in form yet maternal in aspect. Penrose immediately purchased the group.

63

Baga, Guinea
19th century

Nimba Mask

Wood and fibre
122 h
The Trustees of the
British Museum,
London

This spectacular mask was worn over the head of a male dancer who peered through a slot between the breasts. It was used in the rituals of the Simo Society of the Northern Baga following the rice harvest, and represents the transference of female power, associated with fertility, to the male.

64

*Dame Barbara
Hepworth
1903–75*

**Figure of
a Woman**

*1929–30
Corsehill stone
53.3 h
The Trustees of the
Tate Gallery, London*

The reinterpretation of the female nude according to the aesthetics of the new generation of post war modernist sculptors, which included both Henry Moore and Barbara Hepworth, was to be a recurring theme. Hepworth shared with Moore a Yorkshire background and training at Leeds College of Art and the Royal College in London. For both young sculptors the Ethnographical Collection of the British Museum opened up radical ways of depicting the human, especially female form, concentrating on primal power rather than the vapid expressions of feminine fragility and vulnerability promoted in so much public and exhibition sculpture at the time. In 1929 Hepworth had her first child, and it must have come naturally to work on the images of woman and child together, and separately. This figure is carved from fine grained Corsehill stone, which gives a smooth surface with softly rounded curves. Unlike Moore's *Reclining Figure* [65], this sculpture does not make display of female sexuality. It is shown half-length with emphasis on the strong, heavy arms and clasped hands. Despite its comparatively small size, there is a sense of immense strength welling up from inside the body.

65

*Henry Moore
1898–1986*

**Reclining
Figure**

*1929
Brown Hornton stone
84 × 57.2 × 38
Leeds City
Art Galleries*

The figure is both human and geological. It seems to emerge directly from the rough-hewn block of stone (indeed, it is literally doing so). Moore's rejection of white Italian marble, with its traditional associations of softness and purity, in favour of the uncouth textures and blemishes inherent in Hornton stone, a fossilised limestone from Oxfordshire, was part of his repudiation of academic working methods and approaches to interpreting the human form. By tilting the figure forward, he forces the viewer to comprehend it simultaneously from the front and from above, as if looking down from a height on to some rugged island landscape. Ironstone veins run along the body like pathways through valleys and across treeless uplands. The anatomy is utterly distorted by the massive weightiness of the arms and legs; the unnaturally drilled nipples even suggested peaks of volcanic mountains to one contemporary writer ('More Sculpture Monstrosities', *The Daily Mirror*, 14 April 1931). Though the figure is posed like one of Ingres's seductively relaxed and reclining odalisques, by discarding Western classical ideals of female beauty, Moore has created an icon of almost indestructible power.

66

*Helen Chadwick
born 1953*

***Ego Geometria
Sum IX
High School***

*1983
Photographic
emulsion and
plywood
70 × 70 × 70
The artist*

*Helen Chadwick
and Mark
Pilkington*

The Labours IX

*1984
Dyed silver gelatin
photograph
121.9 × 91.4
The artists*

The female nude has long been the prerogative of the male artist. Portrayed as passive, desirable and powerless she has become, and still is, the vehicle for projected male fantasies of female sexuality. This has created problems for women in their efforts to invest the subject with new meaning, drawn from their own experience and free of patriarchal associations. In *Ego Geometria Sum*, Helen Chadwick, avoiding the exploitative nature of the artist/model relationship, uses her own naked body. Her nudity, like that of Eve before the Fall, represents a childhood innocence, a natural state before the trappings of culture. *High School* is one of ten geometrical solids, charting her life, in which 'the shaping forces that constrained the child, arresting and influencing its growth, have compressed the flesh into form'.

The photograph, *Labours IX*, shows the adult artist in contemplative mood embracing her captive self, thus acknowledging her past which she carries with her into the present. Removed from the traditional landscape setting and de-eroticised, her nudity becomes an expression of natural strength which she finds from within herself.

8

Artemisia Gentileschi

Self Portrait as the Art of Painting

4

Elisabeth Louise
Vigée-Le Brun

Self Portrait in
a Straw Hat

5

John William
Haynes

My Pupil

11

Angelica Kauffmann

The Artist Hesitating Between the Arts of Music and Painting

12

Rose Garrard

La Pittura: The Spirit of Painting

17
Giovanni Bellini

**Madonna and Child
with Patron**

19
*Frederick,
Lord Leighton*

**The Music
Lesson**

18
Joseph Wright
(of Derby)

Sarah Carver
and Her
Daughter
Sarah

20

Sir Stanley
Spencer

Hilda, Unity
and Dolls

23

Unknown British painter

Man and Woman in an Interior

24

Frank Holl

The Song of the Shirt

25

Stanhope Forbes

WRNS Ratings Sail-Making

38

*Attributed to
Jan van Scorel*

**Adam and Eve
in the
Garden of Eden**

41

Hugh G. Rivière

**The Garden
of Eden**

40
Arthur Hughes

**The Long
Engagement**

49

Roy Lichtenstein

In the Car

48

Andrea Fisher

In Silence II

44

Sir Lawrence Alma-Tadema

Pleading

43

Henri Gaudier-Brzeska

Woman and Man (Odalisque)

52

Unknown British painter

Armada Portrait of Queen Elizabeth I

54

Paul Brason

Conservative Party Conference 1982

61

Sutapa Biswas

Housewives with Steak-Knives

58

Jonathan Richardson

Lady Mary Wortley Montagu in Turkish Dress

59
Dante Gabriel Rossetti
Astarte Syriaca

60
The Hon John Collier
Clytemnestra

Lenders

8	Her Majesty The Queen
21	The Arts Council of Great Britain
40	Birmingham City Museums and Art Gallery
61	Sutapa Biswas
46	Bowes Museum, Barnard Castle, County Durham
10 16	Brotherton Collection, Leeds University Library
66	Helen Chadwick
18	Derby Art Gallery
17	The Earl of Harewood
58	The Earl of Harrowby
48	Marlene Eleini Gallery
27	Ferens Art Gallery, Hull City Museums and Art Galleries
51	Rachael Field
48	Andrea Fisher
12	Rose Garrard
19 41 44 60	Guildhall Art Gallery, City of London
13	Horniman Museum, London
26	Kirklees Metropolitan Council, Huddersfield Art Gallery
47	Elaine Kowalsky
15 20 23 38 43 50 56 57 62 65	Leeds City Art Galleries
11	Lord St Oswald and The National Trust
29 32 59	Manchester City Art Galleries
1	National Gallery of Ireland
4	National Gallery, London
35	National Museums and Galleries on Merseyside, Lady Lever Art Gallery
3 54	National Portrait Gallery, London
28	Dr and Mrs Richard Pankhurst
42	Private collection
7	Val Robinson
24	Royal Albert Memorial Museum, Exeter
5 39	Scarborough Art Gallery, Scarborough Borough Council
49	Scottish National Gallery of Modern Art, Edinburgh
36	Jo Spence and Terry Dennett
2 9 14 45 55 63	The Trustees of the British Museum, London
25 31 33	The Trustees of the Imperial War Museum, London
53 64	The Trustees of the Tate Gallery, London
52	W. Tyrwhitt-Drake, Esq.
30	Whitworth Art Gallery, University of Manchester
34	York City Art Gallery

Performances by the artist:

22	Bobby Baker
6	Françoise Sergy
37	Silvia Ziranek

Photograph Credits

* 8 *Fig 4*	Reproduced by Gracious Permission of Her Majesty The Queen
21	The Arts Council Collection
* 40	The City of Birmingham Museums and Art Gallery
* 61	Sutapa Biswas
46	The Bowes Museum
* 19 * 24 * 41 * 44 * 60	The Bridgeman Art Library
2 9 14 45 55 63	The British Museum
28	A. C. Cooper
Fig 5	Courtauld Institute of Art
* 5 39	Crescent Museums Photographic Service, Scarborough
* 18	Derby Art Gallery
* 58	The Earl of Harrowby
24	Exeter Museums
27	Ferens Art Gallery
51	Rachael Field
* 48	Andrea Fisher
* 12	Rose Garrard
62	The Henry Moore Foundation
13	Horniman Museum
26	Huddersfield Art Gallery
66	Sean Hudson
* 25 31 33 *Fig 2*	Imperial War Museum
* 17	Jim Kershaw
47	Elaine Kowalsky
* 11 * 38 * 43	Larkfield Photography
* 23 50 65	Leeds City Art Galleries
10 16	Leeds University Photographic Services
29 32 * 59	Manchester City Art Galleries
35	John Mills Photography Ltd
* 4 *Fig 1*	National Gallery, London
1	National Gallery of Ireland
* 49	National Galleries of Scotland
35	National Galleries on Merseyside
* 52	National Maritime Museum, Greenwich
3 * 54 *Fig 3*	National Portrait Gallery, London
36 *Fig 6*	Photography Archive Workshop Ltd
15 20 38 43 50	Charles A. H. Pickard & Son, Photographers
42	Martin W. Roberts
7	Glen Segal
6	Françoise Sergy
53 64	Tate Gallery, London
8	Rodney Todd-White & Son
* 58	Wallace Heaton Ltd
* 20 56 57	West Park Studios, Leeds
22	Andrew Whittuck
30	Whitworth Art Gallery
37	R. Wilson (Hair by Kim and Geri at Toni and Guy)
34	York City Art Gallery

In the Car by Roy Lichtenstein
© *DACS 1989*

Leeds City Art Galleries
Calverley Street, Leeds LS1 3AA
West Yorkshire, England

ISBN 0 901981 43 5

Design by Peter McGrath

Printed in Great Britain
by W. S. Maney and Son Limited
Hudson Road, Leeds LS9 7DL